THE ASSIGNMENT

ANTHONY WILLIAMS JR.

Leyah,
We are so proud of you.
Thank you for picking up
the book.
Happy Birthday!!

[signature]

Absolute Author
Publishing House

Publisher: Absolute Author Publishing House

Editor: Dr. Melissa Caudle

Associate Editor: Paul S. Dupre

Printed in the United States of America
Library of Congress Cataloging-in-Publication Data

The Assignment / Williams Jr., Anthony W.

p. cm.

Paperback ISBN: 978-1-64953-459-0

eBook ISBN: 978-1-64953-460-6

❀ Created with Vellum

For the person that's going through struggling times...
just know you are stronger than you could ever imagine

ACKNOWLEDGMENTS

I would be flat out wrong if I didn't acknowledge the people who have supported me along my book writing journey.

First and foremost, I want to acknowledge God for always affording me with purpose, motivation, and direction. At first, I was unsure of the calling for the book, but God made it possible by eliminating distractions and putting me in a place of focus so that I could provide a clear message. I'm forever grateful for being blessed with a strong, hard-working mother, that showed me that effort will always take me far. When I was young, I didn't see the sacrifices that were made for my little sisters and me. I apologize for all the headaches I put her through. I've learned from those mistakes and will always pay it forward.

My family deserves a huge shoutout for all their support and love they've brought me in my life. I see it as an honor and privilege to have a family. Big thanks to my wife, Courtney, and my two little minions, Trey and Journey, who are probably destroying my house as we speak. I love you all with everything I have. Just know that every lesson in the book is something that I've come across in life, whether it happened to me directly or I witnessed it.

Remember that life is about exposure. Go see the world, be open to different things, and take care of each other. Thank you for brightening my days with your energy. I love you!

To my proofreading team – Miss Ethel, Ricky, Alyssa, Brandon, and Devan. Thank you all so much for your feedback. Together, we delivered.

To all the readers! Traveling to different countries and meeting people from various cultures has opened my eyes in so many ways. I see that the most common factor among all people, regardless of your race, gender, or age is …. struggle. I'm very familiar with adversity and I hope something in this book inspires you to believe in yourself and know that you can overcome any situation you're in. You are so strong; I believe in you. And remember that fear is a powerful emotion. Never let fear hold you back from taking a step towards something that could change your life for the better. Your greatest experiences are just ahead of you, keep walking.

CHAPTER ONE

I don't know what's going on.
I can't concentrate.
My mind has been all over the place.
Why am I out here struggling like this?
This isn't like me.

Walking off the court was embarrassing. "C'mon Brian! I don't know how we lost two games back-to-back," Donovan said as we stormed towards the street. "I was ballin' on those dudes like Steph Curry, and you were playing like Shaq, not early two thousand's Shaq, like the Shaq right now. And I'm trying to figure out how you got crossed by a girl in middle school with Felicia braids," Donovan said while shaking his head at me. "For real B, when you fell back and your hand hit the ground, I thought you were doing a new TikTok dance." Donovan laughed.

"Aye man, it's hot as hell out here, plus I slipped," I said.

"That's fake news. It's D.C. in the summertime. It's gonna be hot. You just can't hoop anymore," Donovan said.

"If you say so, but real talk, she was low key nice."

"Low key, but you're too big for that. Dang near twice her size, hopefully you'll be straight next time," Donovan said.

"Yea, it's just been a lot on my mi…" Right as I was about to finish my sentence, the sound of police sirens that seemed to be getting closer and closer interrupted me. Seconds later, I looked toward the road to see a black car speed past us, followed by two police cars. They had to be going 100 mph. They should've never built this park so close to a main road.

"Man, it looks like another high-speed chase. I gotta get home. It's getting crazy out here. And what the hell is that?" I kneeled to get a closer look at the pointy object on the edge of the sidewalk.

"Don't act like you haven't seen a used needle before," Donovan casually said.

"Damn sure not this close to the park. This isn't weird to you?"

"Weird? Nah fam. It's not like I walk around barefoot, so I'm not worried about stepping on it."

"I didn't grow up here and seeing this type of stuff isn't normal to me, man. I mean look around. We play basketball damn near every day at this dirty, run-down park. The goals don't have nets, and one of them is likely to fall down the next time Big Ray dunks. And don't even get me started on the buildings we live in down the street. It's horrible, hella bugs, and the trash people barely come to empty the dumpsters."

"Hey man, I get it. It's not ideal for anybody. But bro, it's what we have. Either you can adjust or," he paused before finishing his sentence, "Or don't."

"Yea, I know man." I was getting frustrated. Donovan probably thought I was tripping or going off on one of my little rants again but seeing the needle on the ground really got me hot.

We've been in this neighborhood since my dad went to prison, and I've hated every second of it.

"Brian, you always say I don't care because I don't go off like you," he interrupted my thoughts. "But there is nothing I can do about it. I didn't grow up for part of my life in some rich, fancy neighborhood. I've been here since birth, all seventeen years. Yea, it sucks and the first chance I get I'm going to try and get out, but for right now, this is home. It's home for you too and has been for the last five years. When are you going to accept that?"

I heard what Donovan was saying, but it was going in one ear and out the other. I looked around and saw my younger sister, Alexis, walking towards me. Her clothes were filthy. In the past, when my mom and dad were still together, Alexis could get as dirty as she wanted because we had a bunch of clothes and a washer and dryer at home. Now, we had to go to the laundromat on the corner, where half the machines didn't work, and it smelled like booty and band-aids. It may be weeks before Alexis can wear this shirt again.

"Hey, are you done with your game?" Alexis asked when she reached us.

"Yea, you ready to go home?"

"Yea. I'm starving. We played kickball, and I burned off all my food and a lot of calories. I'm thirsty too. I drank all my water five minutes into the game."

My sister is so smart, listen to her talking about burning calories. When I was thirteen years old, I had no idea what a calorie was.

"Alright, go get your bike and we can head home. Yo bro, are you walking with us?" I asked Donovan.

"Yea, most def man. The stock market is about to close soon, and my cousin told me to cop some stocks before going into the weekend."

"Some stocks? Since when you started doing stocks?"

"Ummmm, about two months ago, bro. I've been learning from my cousin since he got out of juvie for selling drugs. He changed his life and started diving into stocks and crypto. At first, I only joined in to support him, thinking it would help him stay out of trouble, but then I really started to see the money I put through the apps grow like crazy. Between Exchange Traded Funds and the dividends the companies are paying me, I don't know how to act," Donovan said with a huge grin on his face.

"Soon, I'll have the dividends paying my cellphone bill. Investing is a life hack bro."

"Sounds interesting, D."

"Whenever you're ready, Brian, we can chop it up more, but let's walk faster. I gotta get to these stocks then I need to listen to the new Drake album. I heard it's tough."

"Yea, they say it's hard."

Can't believe Donovan is getting into stocks. He was the most gangster, hidden geek I've ever seen in my life. One time we had to break up a fight between him and the head football coach at school because he told Donovan that he had to wear a mouthpiece in the game and not the iced-out, gold grill that he bought from the mall. Then, when I took Alexis to the library the next day to get a book, I saw him taking Blockchain technology classes online when he thought no one was around.

As we walked home, I purposely didn't bring up our living conditions, I hated for Alexis to hear me complaining. I can tell she looks up to me, and in a way that makes me want to strive to do better. But truth be told, I don't know what I would do without her. She's so dependable and smart. I've always struggled to read and write in school, and I'm horrible at taking tests. I've even taken a few remedial classes throughout middle and high school. It's helped a little, but luckily Alexis has always been years ahead of her time. This year, I had to lean heavy on my sister to help me with my assignments. The coach told me I was going to be kicked off the team if I failed anymore classes. Alexis stepped up big time and told me I wouldn't have to worry about it. I would never tell Donovan this. If he found out I needed my little sister to help me with my homework, he would clown me for weeks.

We hadn't been back home for a good ten minutes, and Alexis was already starting the hungry talk. I can't blame her. She already told me she worked off her food at the park. Mama left a note on the fridge for me to feed her but didn't say what. Mama also hasn't been to the grocery store and as I open the fridge, I didn't see much of anything in here. Maybe she forgot. I know she's stressed out with working two jobs and lately her mind has been all over the place.

Things have been rough over the last five years since my pops left. My mom has been trying to display a hard front, but I know she's hurting as well. She's never allowed us to see her cry tears, and she's always telling me to "man up." I hate it. Even when I'm feeling down, she says, "Be tough so you can survive in this world." Like, a few months back, when my teammate was hit by a stray bullet, just walking back from the store after a game. He was in the hospital for weeks. The bullet hit him two inches from his heart. He almost bleed to death before the ambulance arrived. I could tell my mom was just as hurt as I was, her and his mother got their check cashed at the same spot. When I came to my mom about the incident, her eyes watered, then she ran to her room and shut the door. She knew that could've easily been me.

I knocked on the door to ask her if she was okay, but she ignored my question and told me to take the trash out, as if seeing her cry would be a sign of weakness. She told me in the past that I had to be hard to make it in this neighborhood, but I would rather just hug and hear my mom tell me she loves me, even cry a little. Instead, since my dad left, I've only been pushed further away. She's wants to be mom and dad. But I feel like I don't have either anymore.

I've had to step up to help raise Alexis. There's been times where there was only sliced bread to eat for dinner. Like yesterday, I told Alexis she could eat both remaining slices, because I knew I would get a free lunch at my school the next day, and for some reason her middle school didn't offer that. When we first moved, my grandma used to send us care packages with snacks and different kinds of foods we could use for meals. However, now those packages come once every blue moon. I'm not complaining about not getting the food. Granny is on a fixed income, but I sure miss how she used to look out for us. Alexis is going to kill me if I don't figure out what's for dinner tonight. This really makes me angry. It's my fourth time opening the refrigerator, and I was lowkey hoping that something would magically appear. Like some Kool-Aid, steak, or homemade mac and cheese would be nice. Let me stop. We're so broke at the moment, I can't even think about food. There is nothing in the cabinets either, wait… ahh we have Ramen Noodles. They are so far in the back; I hope they are still good. "Hell yea!" I breathed out a sigh of relief when I looked at the date. Dang! I thought there were two packages but there is only one. It's cool. At least Alexis would be able to eat.

Things used to be so different back then, I thought to myself. I was young in the picture of me sitting on my dad's lap and my mom holding Alexis. Looking at this picture is bittersweet. It's when my parents were still together, and my mother wasn't working multiple jobs. Back when we had money, and spent a lot of time together, vacations, amusement parks, and running in the sprinklers in the summer. Things weren't perfect by any means. My dad still drank a lot, but we were happy. Happy as a family. My sister used to smile a lot more back then too.

But when my father went to prison, everything I knew about life changed. My dad had been in jail before, but it usually was only for a few months at a time. This time was way more serious. Last month, my grandma told me he got out of prison over a year ago. Part of me doesn't want to believe it. Surely, he would've came back to us, at least for Alexis and me. My mom, well, maybe not so much. She divorced him as soon as he got sentenced to years in prison. She told us she was tired of that lifestyle, and that what he was doing wasn't fair to me and Alexis. I was upset for months. I wouldn't talk to her. Hell, I wouldn't even look at her. I couldn't see why she would do something like that to him, to us, to our family. I had to put myself in her shoes. It took me a while to understand why she made that decision. I'm not saying it was the right choice, but I can see where she was coming from. I could tell my dad was hurt by her choice as well. Before he left, my dad was the happiest person I knew. He was always smiling and playing around with Lex and me. But after he got locked up, his entire attitude changed and he stopped calling us. Now, it's been over three years since I've heard his voice.

If I ever see him again, I'm going to ask him why he never came back to see us. Why would he put himself in situations that could cause him to go to jail? I have so many questions and so many answers that I need from him.

Last year, for prom, I had to learn how to tie my bowtie from YouTube. I would've asked Donovan's dad, but he's on drugs and my mom told me I can't be around him. There's not a lot of men in my community. I don't really know why that is. In my old neighborhood, there were plenty and all races too. Black, Brown, White, purple, yellow, you name it. Well, not really purple, but you get the picture. It seemed like everybody helped each other out, but here everybody is out for themselves. It's hard to trust people in this neighborhood. People sometimes make fun of me for the way that I speak. They say, I sound like a White boy, like what the hell does that even mean? "Damn, I hate it here!" I said out loud.

Alexis was in her room, so she couldn't hear me. Thank goodness. I miss my dad, but I'm also pissed at him. I hope he still loves us. I don't know where he is, but maybe if I find him, he'll come back home, and things can go back to normal. Maybe mama can stop working so hard and have time to relax and have fun again, like how it was before.

"Brian are you upstairs?" Alexis called out.

Where else would I be?

"Yea, what is it?"

"Your boy Donovan is here, and I want to go outside to ride my bike."

Alexis knows she can't go outside alone, and I'm not in the mood to go out but I know I can't keep her cooped up in the house all day, plus it's been a few days since I've seen Donovan so I guess I can go out.

"Okay, Lex, you can go outside but stay on the street where I can see you. We're going to sit outside in front of the building."

At thirteen, I know Lex is definitely old enough to play outside without supervision, but she's my responsibility when mama isn't home. She's a pretty girl, with big beautiful brown eyes. She's petite and looks like a child to me, but that doesn't mean anything to the boys in this neighborhood. Half the lil' girls around here are dating men twice their age, and that won't be my sister. As long as I'm outside, they leave her alone.

Every house that we have lived in my mom has always hung this sign up above her door: "Walk by faith, not by sight." I don't know who said this, but I'm staring at it every day, more and more. The other day, I didn't get to tell Donovan what my plan was, but since he's here, I'll tell him now.

"What's up, man?" I asked Donovan as we did our special handshake.

"Nothing much. I came to see what you were up to. Babysitting I see."

"Something like that. I babysit you too, don't I?"

Donovan laughed and shook his head. "Whatever you say."

"Aye bro, you talk to Christina?" He asked.

"No man, why do you keep asking about me and her? You want me to get with her so bad, don't you?"

"Why not? She likes you, man."

"I like her, but I'm not trying to get into no relationship right now, we literally just graduated, and my mom told me, 'Brian, you can either go to the Army or go to college, but you gotta get the hell out of my house.' So, I'm in the process of trying to figure things out."

"Damnnnn, your mama told you that?"

"Yes bro, ruthless, she told me she wants to turn my room into a woman's cave, whatever the hell that is."

"Brian, man, I think you should give Christina a shot. She's smart as hell. Cute, and accepts you for you."

"If she's so cute, why don't you holla at her?"

"Too short, way too short, man. You know I like tall girls. I'm trying to build a basketball team. My woman got to at least be six feet tall," Donovan said while laughing.

"Bro, you a fool. I don't know if this is a good time."

"When is a good time, then?"

"Aye, bro, let's sit here on the stoop for a second."

"Okay, you good?" He asked me with concern in his voice.

"Yo, Dee, I think I'm going to go find my dad." I breathed in deeply. "No, I am going to go find him. I'm tired of living like this."

"Here you go with this again. It's always something with you and this place. What are you tired of? Your setup isn't that bad. You have a roof over your head, air conditioning, running water. There are so many kids who wished they had a portion of what you have and you're just going to give it all up to go find your dad."

"That's the thing you don't get, Donovan. It's not about what I currently have. It's about what I had before. I must bring my family back together."

"Why would you want to leave that for someone who didn't care to come back to you when he got out of jail? How do you know your father wants to be found?" His face had confusion written all over it. I knew he didn't understand.

"I don't know if my dad wants to be found, but maybe he does. Maybe he doesn't know where we are."

Deep down, I know Donovan is making a good point about my dad not coming back, but I can't allow myself to think that he doesn't want us. He has to.

"What's going to happen to your sister while you're on this journey to find your dad??

"I'm going to take her with me,"

"Man, now you're tripping!" He said as he wiped the sweat from his face. "Let me get this straight, Brian. So, you're just going to leave your mom and take her daughter with you? She's going to call the police the moment she gets home and realizes neither one of you is here. You know she's strict about you being in before dark."

"I'm going to leave her a note. man,"

"Woowwww, a note. Bad idea, man! Listen, I'm not trying to call you dumb, but you're not exactly the brightest crayon in the box. You don't even make decent grades; I don't know how they let you play football last year. The best thing you have going for yourself right now is that you're big as hell. Nobody is going to mess with you at six feet four, weighing in over two-hundred and thirty. But, you don't know the first thing about living on your own. Most importantly, you don't have any money. How will the two of you survive?" He stressed.

I'm really getting annoyed by Donovan's comments and lack of faith. He's doubting me and that just makes me want to do it even more. He doesn't know what he's talking about. I'm going to find my dad and bring him back. I'll prove him wrong, and he'll be the one looking crazy.

"We'll make it. My dad has a brother that doesn't live too far and maybe if we can get to him, he can take us to our dad."

"Okay man, I don't know who you've been talking to, but you're really wildin' right now." Donovan shook his head in disbelief.

"D, check this out. A while back, Principal Thompson came to our class, and he mentioned the importance of having a vision and the significance of time."

"Huh?"

"I know it sounds different. But I trust it and I trust him. After hearing his speech to our class, I learned that I've been moving through life without purpose, and having a vision gives us the direction that we need. We have to create a vision so strong that it's like a sneak peek of what's to come in the future. Can't be there physically yet, so we have to do it mentally and emotionally."

"Hold up, bro. What are you talking about? Mentally and emotionally?"

"Donovan, feel me on this. I'm still learning but he said we have to position ourselves in the vision without physically being there, and lately, bro, I've been living in the moment of being with my father again. I breathe and smell the air that he breathes and smells. I can see him and how happy he is to be with us again. But I have to put action towards this vision. If I don't, it's just a dream."

"Man, you're really reaching."

"Chill out, bro. I'm serious."

"Well, what did Principal Thompson say about time?" he sarcastically asked me.

"He told us that when you start seeing time as a luxury, your life changes immediately. That hit me deep, man. Because I know I've been playing around with my time. Watching T.V. or daydreaming about things that don't matter. My grades would've looked way better if I had actually put forth the effort. That's time I can't get back."

"Yea man, I struggle with time as well," he admitted.

I was shocked because he was so good at a lot of stuff.

"Man, real talk a lightbulb went off in my head this day and I sat up in my chair when the principal said that time is the world's currency and how you spend it determines your outcome in life. I realize that everything is connected to how you spend your time and it's something you can never get back. I don't want to be one of these guys out here always saying how they were the man in high school, but since then they haven't done anything with their lives. If I don't use my time wisely, I will continue to struggle bro and my sister will continue to go hungry. I can't have that man. I have to figure something out."

"Brian, I see what you're saying, but is finding your dad really a smart move? That's all I'm saying."

I'm not going to convince Donovan that my plan is a good idea. He will just have to see it when it's done. I see Alexis walking back over, so I say, "Let's talk about this later. I haven't told Alexis and I don't want her flipping out."

"Brian, can we walk down to Ms. Janet's house? Yesterday, she told mama she had some stuff for us," Alexis asked.

"Oh really? Alright, let's go."

I wondered what Ms. Janet had, she always gave us good stuff. As we were walking, I thought to myself, *Maybe D was right. I've never been an A student. What if I get Alexis and I hurt, or worst, killed? For some reason, my gut isn't telling me this is a bad move. I feel like it would if I was out of it.*

Luckily, Ms. Janet's apartment was only a two-minute walk from ours.

"Alexis, hurry up and get what you need to get from Ms. Janet. It's getting dark, and I want to get back home."

"So now you're afraid of the dark," Donovan whispered so Alexis couldn't hear him. He continued, "You better get used to it if you plan on running away. The sun isn't going to not go down just because you're outside."

"Just chill out, man, damn!" I raised my voice.

Alexis looked back to see why I was yelling. I waited until she had turned back around before I continued. This time, whispering, "Haven't you ever wanted a better life? I already have to feed Lex when we get home, and I don't even know what's in there. Get off my back about it. I should have never said anything to you."

"Whatever! Brian, don't make a temporary decision that will have a permanent outcome. You may not be a genius, but you are for sure smarter than this. I'm not going to tell you that I support a bad idea because I don't. You know my brother is in jail for selling drugs because he felt like he had to do something to better his situation too. Look how that turned out. Obviously, I can't talk you out of it, so I'll say a prayer for the Big Man to protect you. But I still think it's crazy."

Alexis comes back outside empty handed. "What happened Lex?"

"Ms. Janet ran out of cake and juice. She said for us to come back in three days."

"Dang, okay. You can walk ahead, I gotta finish talking to D."

"Alrighty."

"Aye man, I'm not your brother, and I'm not going to be selling drugs. You won't be saying that when I come back with my dad," I said confidently to Donovan, making sure Alexis couldn't hear me.

"Okay Brian, whatever you say. When are you thinking about leaving, anyway?"

"Not sure. I just thought of the idea a few days ago. Once I figure out a plan, I'll take off. Just keep this between me and you for right now."

"Yea, man, I'm going to head home. Be safe. I'll catch you later. I hope." He sounded like this would be the last time he saw me.

CHAPTER TWO

Leyah

A few hours later, I   I heard
my mom come in.

"Hey baby, how was your day? It's kind of late for you to still
be up."

I didn't respond.

"Young man, do you hear me talking to you?"

I'm not answering her. She can see on my face that I'm upset.

She walked over to the T.V. and turned it off. Now she's
looking right at me. "I know you hear me, why are you not
answering me? I know it's summer, but it's about time for you to
be headed to bed. I'm not raising any disrespectful children."

"You're not raising me at all," I mumbled.

"Excuse me, what was that? Suddenly, you have something to
say?"

"I said," my voice shaking, "you're not raising me at all. You
work all the time and you're barely home." I sat up straight. I just
wanted to be prepared to block in case she tried to slap me in my
mouth for talking crazy, but I can't keep my thoughts to myself
any longer.

"Brian, what is that supposed to mean? I'm the only one
taking care of you. If I don't work, you don't eat."

"Well, you're doing all this working and I'm still not eating. Not for real. You told me to feed Alexis, but I had to find an old pack of noodles to give her because there were literally no groceries in the kitchen. The fridge is empty. There was nothing left for me to eat tonight or last night." Tears welled up in my eyes, but I pushed them back. I'm practically a man, and I know she wouldn't allow me not to be tough.

"Wha...?" She started to say something, but I could see on her face that she realized she'd forgotten to go to the grocery store. "...You're right, I forgot to get groceries. I'm sorry about that, but that's no excuse for you to take this tone of voice with me. I'm still your mother and you will be respectful under my household, where I pay all the bills. Now, it's late and not much is open, but I can run to the corner store and get you something quick to eat and then I'll make sure to get some groceries tomorrow."

"Just forget it," I started, "I'll just go to bed hungry." I ran to my bedroom, softly closing the door. I wanted to slam the door, but I didn't want to give her a reason to come to my room.

I sat on the floor with my head in between my legs, crying like I've never cried before. I heard a door slam. I knew my mom was upset. I shouldn't have yelled like that. I know she's trying her best. Things are rough right now. After about fifteen minutes or so, I stood up and looked in the mirror. My eyes looked swollen from all the crying.

My emotions were high with anger and disappointment, and not to mention my stomach was growling. I felt like my stomach was touching my back. I laid down, but I kept tossing and turning. I didn't tell my mom about how Alexis started crying when she realized she had to eat noodles for dinner yesterday. She hates noodles. It wasn't even enough to fill her stomach, so she went to bed hungry, too. Tonight, she had cereal, but that wasn't any better. "How am I going to get us out of this?" I breathed out loud. I heard my mom telling my godmother that she heard that my father was living in Texas. That's the last place he was transferred to while in federal prison. That's a long way from

Washington, D.C. It'll take us ages and probably cost a lot of money. I don't have a dime to my name because I'm not allowed to get a job. Mama always said my job was watching Lex. If she had just allowed me to get a job while I was in school, we wouldn't be living nearly as bad as we do now. Come to think about it, two years ago there was a postcard on the refrigerator from our dad's brother, Uncle. My mom got upset one day and removed it, but I've kept it under my dresser since then.

It says, "Just know we are always thinking of you all... with love, from Atlanta." Okay, he lives in Atlanta. There isn't an address attached, but at least I know what city he's in. It's been about four years since we've seen him. I remember two things about Uncle Eric. He was always a super nice person, but his wife… I laughed and shook my head. She hated us. I don't know how Uncle Eric could stand being married to such an evil woman. She makes Cruella De Vil look like Mother Teresa. I don't know what it is, but it's like she hates kids. Maybe she's changed, maybe not. But Uncle Eric is the only way to my dad. Regardless, I think this is the reason that I've been noticing the "walk by faith, not by sight" sign every day in our home. It's time I stop being scary and go with the feeling I have in my gut. That's what we'll do, we'll go to Uncle Eric's. He has to know where my dad is.

I'm feeling energized this morning. It's a new day with new opportunities and I'm ready for a change. First, I have to tell Alexis my plan. Hopefully, she's more on board than Donovan was. I go into the kitchen to find Alexis already up and eating. Mama must have gone to the grocery store before she left for work. Great because Lex is happiest when she's eating. I can't talk to her about anything when she's even the slightest bit hangry.

"Brian, mama went to the store, and she got my favorite cereal. It's so much better than that sugarless cereal I ate last night," she said with the biggest smile on her face.

"I see. That's good! I want to talk to you about something."

"Okay, what's up?"

"Do you miss daddy?" I'm starting with this to gauge how she might react to what I'm about to say.

"Yes. Do you know when he's coming back?" She asked, while looking down in her bowl of cereal.

"I don't. Does it make you sad that he's not here?"

"A little. I didn't get to spend a lot of time with him. He's been gone for a long time, and I wish he would come back. We used to have so much fun together."

"Yea, I remember all the fun. What do you think about us leaving and going to find him?"

Her eyes got wide, "Umm, I think mommy is going to kill us if she comes home and we're not here."

"What? Why would you think that? Don't you want to find daddy?"

"I heard a little bit about what you and Donovan were talking about yesterday. It's not that I don't want daddy to come home, but I kind of agree with him. I don't think going to find him is the smartest idea." She hesitated a little, as if she was thinking about what she wanted to say.

"Seriously? I know she'll be upset, but I think if we can find him, then our life will get better. I don't want you having to eat noodles for the rest of your life. Maybe in the end, when things work out, mama won't be as mad."

"Maybe. Do you know where he is?"

"I'm not really sure. But do you see the man on this card?" I took Uncle Eric's postcard out of my pocket.

"Yea, that's daddy's brother, right?"

"Yea, he lives in Atlanta. It's only about eleven hours from here."

"Eleven hours?"

"About, give or take. I want us to go, and I know I don't have any money, but I do know someone that works at the bus station. My homeboy, Sean. He might be able to get us some tickets. Then when we get down to Atlanta, we can find Uncle E and he can direct us exactly to daddy."

"Brian, I think this is a crazy idea, but if you really think it's worth a try, then I'll go with you. I miss Daddy and I could really use one of his tight bear hugs right now. I have hundred and seventy dollars in my piggy bank. Maybe that will help us,"
    I almost dropped my drink. "Where did you get money from?" We've gone without food and all this time, and you've been keeping money in your piggy bank.
    "I've had it for years. It's birthday money, and I was saving it for the right time. This seems like a good time." She was so nonchalant about it, as if we didn't just go to bed hungry.
    "Wow, Alexis. You never cease to amaze me. This is a great time. When you're done eating, please pack your backpack with a few clothing items and whatever else will fit. Also, put some of these snacks that mama just got us in there too, so we'll have food. I'll pack my bag and we'll leave right after. I'm going to leave a note on the fridge."
    I'm excited and nervous that Lex is on board, but there is no way I could do this without my sister. This plan had to work, if not for me, then for Alexis. She deserves so much more. I'm determined to get that for her.
    We got our stuff together and then as I almost forgot, I scribbled a note on the back of an old envelope that was on the table.

Dear Mama, I love you so much. We're going to find daddy. Please DO NOT call the police. We'll be back soon. I promise to take care of Alexis. Trust me on this. I Love You – Brian

I placed the note on the refrigerator, and we walked out the door not realizing the difficult journey which lay ahead.

CHAPTER THREE

The nearest Greyhound bus station was about ten minutes from the house. When we got there, I didn't see my boy, Sean. I panicked a little. I should have called before I came to see if he was working today. Dang, what if he isn't working? What if he got fired or left for the summer?

"I'm sure Sean is around here somewhere. Probably went to the bathroom really quick," I told Alexis.

"You didn't call him before we came? Do you even know when the bus is supposed to leave? What if it doesn't leave until tomorrow? I thought you planned this out, Brian?" Oh, my goodness, she's asking all these questions.

I couldn't answer her right now while I was searching for Sean. My head is moving so quickly, like it's on a swivel. I should've thought this out a little better. I thought everything would fall into place once we got to the bus station. This was my first step. Or was my first step supposed to be calling Sean to make sure he was working? I have to figure this out. We were just starting this journey, and I didn't want her to lose faith in me.

"Never mind, there he is right over there." I have never been so relieved. I just pray the bus to Atlanta is leaving sooner than later. "Big Sean, what's up, man?" I had never called him "Big

Sean" before. He was only 5'5", on a good day. But I felt the need to elevate him, so he could slide us some bus tickets for our trip.

"What's up King! It's good to see you. Are you and you sis taking a trip?" He asked me.

"Yea, but how have you been, bro? How is the family... oowww?!" I yelped, as Alexis looks up at me, pressing down on my big toe with her foot, giving me the death stare for making small talk. I get it, but it was rude to not ask someone how they were doing. She knew that.

"You okay, man? Everybody is good. How can I help you?" Sean said while grinning.

"We do need a little help. I really want to find my dad; however, I don't know where he is, but I know his brother lives in Atlanta, Georgia." I hesitated before continuing, and looked around to make sure no one was listening, "Do you think you can help us out with two tickets? Is there a bus going to Atlanta?"

"Hold up, Brian," he double checked his watch. "You wildin' man! I can't believe you're really gonna roll up on me and ask me for a hand out. But you did save me that one time in 5th grade when my *Yo Mama* jokes on Fat J went too far. Man, you're in luck." With a huge smile on his face he said, "It just so happens that two people just bought tickets to go to Atlanta and then they came back and told us they weren't going to be able to make the bus ride. The tickets are non-refundable so they couldn't get the money back. The bus is leaving in about ten minutes and you two can get right on."

"Stop playing. Are you serious?!" I couldn't believe what I was hearing. This news made me feel like this journey was meant to be.

"Yep, it's crazy, right! Come on, I'll walk you to the bus because I don't want you to miss it!"

We're so lucky this worked out this way. It's like it was meant to be and that everything is going to work out. What are the chances that they had two unused tickets on the day we showed up?

"How long is the ride?" Alexis asked Sean.

"It's about fourteen hours. They'll stop and take breaks so you can get food and use the restroom. I know it's still kind of early, but if you try to sleep, it'll go by fast," he told her. He knew fourteen hours sounded like a long time to be on a bus and Alexis did, too.

"I brought my favorite book, so I'll read it to keep busy. Does Uncle Eric know we're coming?" she asked me.

Here we go again with the questions. "No," I paused for a few seconds. I didn't want to tell Alexis that I didn't even know if our uncle was in town. If I told her that, she might turn around and go back home.

"Not yet, I'll call him a little later."

It's time for me to cut the tough guy act and stop pretending like I had everything worked out. She would eventually pick up on it, anyway. I paused for a moment. "Alexis, in all honesty, I don't have his phone number. I don't know where he lives, but I brought the picture and I hope someone will be able to direct us to his house. I'm really just moving on faith now."

Alexis nodded her head in agreement, but I could tell she was a little worried that I was taking her on a wild goose chase.

She began walking and looked back at me and said, "I trust you."

We jumped on the bus and grabbed seats near the back. As the bus rolled out of the parking lot, I looked over at Alexis as she closed her eyes and placed her hand over her heart. She would do this from time to time. I noticed the words that she mouthed, "I'm exactly where I'm supposed to be." I smiled and closed my eyes, but only to sleep. I've been up most of the night, and exhausted is an understatement. Before I fell into a deep sleep, I thought to myself how Alexis has been walking by faith her entire life and that I had to step up as a brother and guide us towards our purpose.

I was fast asleep and almost fell out of the chair when I heard a loud, squeaky voice on the bus's speaker. "Rest stop everybody.

We'll be here for twenty minutes. If you want to get off, stretch your legs, get food or use the bathroom, now is the time to do so."

I looked over at Alexis and she was putting her book back into her backpack. "I need to use the bathroom," she said to me.

"Okay, we'll go inside. Take your stuff with you. We don't know these people and they might try to steal our bags if we leave them on the bus," I said in a deep, macho voice. I wanted anyone listening to know I didn't play. The sun was beaming outside. It had to be around 5:00 p.m. or so. I noticed a sign that said: "Welcome to Fayetteville, North Carolina." I thought to myself, *Wow, I'm in Fayetteville.* I had never been out of D.C. before. Well, only to PG County, Maryland to see my grandmother, but this is different. This is so dope, and I wondered if the hip-hop artist, J. Cole, would be somewhere nearby. I was literally listening to his last album yesterday. Crazy, his first song on the album mentions something about riding on I-95. We had been riding on I-95 for hours before arriving in "the Ville." No one can tell me this isn't destiny.

When I walked inside the bus terminal, I was shocked with how big it was. "Let's meet back here in five minutes."

We went our separate ways. While I was looking around, I looked out the window to see the most beautiful girl in the world walking toward the entrance from outside. We had to be about the same age. She had long black hair with beautiful, smooth skin. It's something about the way the sun was shining on her. That Fayetteville sun hits differently.

I wanted to talk to her, but I had to position myself accordingly. Can't be right at the front of the terminal. I didn't want to seem too thirsty. She might be the one. God knows exactly what he did when he created her. As she walked by, I gave her a smile. For some reason, she didn't smile back, but she looked at me. It's cool, let me relocate. I can't get my eyes off this girl. She's a whole vibe. I wish she would take out her earbuds so I could say something to her. Maybe I'll hit her with a, "Yo, Miss Lady?" or maybe I'll ask her for directions like, "Excuse me, beautiful, how do you get back to I-95?" Nah, that won't work. I'm at a bus terminal, nobody has cars over here, that's why we are taking the bus! Why would I need directions? I feel like I'm stalking her with all this moving around I'm doing. I gotta figure something out, quick!

Hold up, where is Alexis? It's been five minutes and she is nowhere in sight.

Damn, I'm over here checking for ole girl and I've messed around and lost my sister. I started calling her name and looking around. I know she can't still be in the bathroom.

"Alexis, Alexis!" As I'm about to walk over to the cashier ask them to call for her over the loudspeaker. I say her name one last time, "Alexis!"

"Fool, I'm right here." She was less than two feet away from me. I didn't even see her short self.

"I said be back in five minutes. Why are you late?"

"I'm barely late. I was in the bathroom. Were you worried?"

"No, no, I'm good." She was getting smart, and it wasn't the time, especially with my beautiful angel in here walking around, "I'm just making sure you're straight."

"I'm fine," she said. She seems tired and annoyed. She's probably hungry.

I'm hungry too, but I want to save the snacks we brought from home. "Do you want to get something hot? We can find something cheap, quick, and share it. That way we can save the snacks for later," I asked her.

"Maybe. I am a little hungry. But I don't want us to run out of money. What if we need it later?"

"We're not going to spend all of it. Not even half of it. We have enough," I reassured her.

"Okay, what about that place over there? The burger place," she suggested.

I looked at the menu for the burger place. It had a dollar menu and if we each got three items, burger, fries, and drinks, that would only be six dollars. If we kept eating like this, then the money would last for a while.

"Do you want a milkshake?" I asked because I wanted one, but Alexis had all the money.

"We don't have to buy everything we see," Alexis said. Alexis has always been good with money. Clearly, she only spends money when she has to. She gets that from our mom. Both can be cheap as hell. I'm like my dad. When I have money, I want to buy what I want, when I want it. You only live once.

"Lex, it's only two dollars. Let me borrow it, I'll pay you back. Chill out."

She handed me the money and grabbed a table in the corner. From the looks of the other tables, it looked the cleanest. Getting the food was quick and when the cashier handed me the burgers and milkshake, I turned to the lids counter. There she was again, my future. I want to call this love at first sight, but she won't look at me. I'll turn in my playa card right now if she just say's what's up. I can see us with a whole family. Five kids running in the backyard, playing tag. Us drinking lemonade on the porch with our toes out. People walking down the street saying things like, 'I see you Brian'. Me hitting them back with the nod.

I can change her life. I'm curious why she's standing alone and smiling so hard. She must've glanced at me when I looked down. Let me step a little closer. I overheard her say she'll talk to them later. Yea, I was ear hustling. I gotta catch her before she walks away. Bump it, I'm going to say something. My dad always said, you miss every shot you don't shoot. Usually that was meant for basketball, but today I'm relating it to wifey.

"Excuse me. Umm. Hey, I'm Brian," I said, grabbing two lids and trying to play it cool.

"Boy bye, I have a man." she rudely said.

"Yea, me too."

She power walks away from the counter toward the exit. I thought she was gonna at least look back. Damn. Whatever. I walk over to our table. I hope Alexis didn't hear anything.

"Hey Brian," she says when I sit down.

"Hey, Lex,"

"So, you got a man, too?"

Damn. I was wrong. She heard me. We burst out laughing.

"No, she caught me off guard."

Never thought I would think this but, I guess it's a good thing she blew me off. Right now, I don't have time for girls. I should be focused on getting us to Atlanta. I took a strong sip of my strawberry milkshake the moment I sat down. Whoa! Now I have a brain freeze, but it was worth it. This milkshake tastes like memories. It reminded me of why I was leaving home. It also reminds me of the milkshakes I used to get by our old house. I can't remember the last time I ate anything that wasn't at home because we never had any extra money to eat out. I ate my food fast. I still hadn't hit the restroom, so I got up to do that really quick. I was in there a little longer than usual. Must've been the dairy. It had my stomach bubbling. Last time, at my grandma's house, I had a big bowl of vanilla ice-cream. It tasted good but had me on the toilet, back and forth for two days. My grandmother said I'm lactose-something. I should've known better than to drink that milkshake. Three minutes later, I hear a knocking at the door. "Brian, come on," Alexis said.

"Okay, I'm coming Lex. Give me one sec." I got up and went to the sink to wash my hands. No issues. But as I start walking toward the door, I felt my stomach rumble. Then out of nowhere it did a weird Mortal Kombat front flip, Dragon Ball Z spinning kick, and forced me to leapfrog back to the toilet. I'm just glad no one saw that. I pretty much jumped over the stall door to sit down. A few more minutes went by. I looked down and saw that I had completely kicked my shoes off. Enough, must take back control of my body. I started walking. I felt okay, I guess. Maybe this time it's not as bad. I walked up to Alexis and grabbed her hand, intending to guide her to where we had last saw the bus.

She immediately snatched it back. "Oh no, Brian, did you wash your hands? You don't look so good," she said.

"I'm fine. Let's just get to the bus. And yes, I did wash my hands."

When we got outside, I didn't see the bus. I felt myself panicking, but I couldn't let Lex see me scrambling again.

"Where is our bus? It was right here!" Alexis asked. I could hear the worry in her voice.

"I'm not sure. Don't panic, let me ask someone. Maybe we are in the wrong place."

I saw a man moving cones by another bus and asked him where our bus was.

"I'm sorry, man, that bus pulled out five minutes ago?"

"What! The driver said we had twenty minutes. I've been checking my watch. Can he come back?"

"I don't know what happened. Maybe you got the times wrong, but he left here on time. He can't come back because it'll put him off schedule," he responded and kept putting the cones away. He didn't seem to care.

"What do I do now? I have my little sister with me. I don't have any way to leave here."

"I feel for you, man," the guy said, "but I can't help you. The only thing I can tell you is to go inside to the man at the cash register. He's been working at this bus terminal for a long time. He might be able to get you on another bus."

"Oh okay, thanks."

Man, how could I be so stupid? How could I let time slip away from me? My mom has been telling me, "Brian, time is the only real true currency. Treat it with care, Brian. To be on time is to be late." I can hear her voice ringing in my ear. Yea, my stomach got the best of me, but before that I was over there checking for a girl that doesn't even want me. In a whole relationship, but I still had to holla. I don't even want to face Alexis. She's about to be hot! I'm supposed to be the big brother, but I keep acting like a little boy.

My mind was racing a mile a minute as I walked back over to her. I didn't know what to tell her or how to tell her we had missed our bus. I knew nothing about where we were. I knew it had to be at least a couple hours away since this was the second stop after Richmond, Virginia. I thought about calling my mom and telling her what happened, but that would just add more stress to her life. If she came to get us, we would still have to wait, and she would be extremely upset because she would have to take off work.

"We missed our bus, didn't we?" Alexis cried.

"Please don't cry, Lex. I got this, don't cry. I'm sorry, I don't know how this happened. But I'm going to figure it out."

Alexis is smart and courageous for coming with me, but her crying is making me feel like crap.

"I'll figure it out, I promise. Dry your eyes and let's go inside."

CHAPTER FOUR

A few hours later, Alexis and I were sitting in the lobby of a nearby motel. It was about a ten-minute walk from the bus stop. When I spoke to the lady at the ticketing counter, she told me the next bus to Atlanta wasn't leaving for another forty-eight hours. Normally, the buses ran twice a day to Atlanta since it was only six hours away, but they were having a shortage of bus drivers, so they had cut the trips down. She also told me she could not guarantee us a seat on the next bus because it was not the station's fault that we missed the bus in the first place. That kind of pissed me off because I really believe the bus driver left early. The other issue was that we did not have a real ticket, and even if we did, we would have to hope the seats were not sold out.

"Can I help you all with something?" A tall, weird looking man asked. He had to be about six foot six. But he was very skinny. If I had to guess, he probably weighed about 170 pounds. I remembered seeing him outside smoking weed when we first walked up. Whatever strain he had was strong, but now I could barely smell it.

"What's up, bro? We missed our bus. I was wondering if you all had any rooms to spare. We don't really have any money," I admitted. Usually I would've held that information close to the chest, but maybe he would have pity on us. I didn't want to use what money we had left for a room if I didn't have to.

"Listen, kid, this isn't a charity or homeless shelter. These rooms cost money and if I give you one for free, other people will come around asking for one."

I looked around to see if he saw something that I didn't. The lobby was empty, and no one had walked in or out since we had been sitting here and we'd been here for about twenty minutes. "There is no one here, so if you help us out, who will know?"

"I'll know, and my manager will know if he comes in tonight," the hotel attendant responded.

I paused and thought about seeing him smoking weed. That had to be illegal. "Well, does your manager know that you're smoking weed on your break and at his hotel?"

I saw his face get red. He must have thought he was out of view, and no one saw him. I could tell he was getting embarrassed. "Yea, I saw you. So, can we get that room or what?"

"My manager won't believe you?" he responded nervously.

"Yea, he probably would. You smell like weed, man. Why would he not believe me? Why would I make this up? Do you really want to test the waters?"

"You can't come in here and try to blackmail me for a room. I should call the cops on you." He was getting angry, but I didn't care.

"And tell them what, that you're doing drugs? You would probably get in just as much trouble as me. Look man, I just want somewhere for my sister and I to lay our heads. I thought maybe you would help me, but since you're not…" I shrugged, trying to think of the next thing I could say to scare him. I didn't have to think for long.

"Okay, okay. I'll give you a room, but if you see me talking to a man in a red collared shirt, it's more than likely my manager, so be cool, or you'll be out."

I made eye contact and nodded at Alexis. I told her I would take care of us. I looked back at the guy, "Hey man. I appreciate it." I never had any intentions of telling his manager in the first place. I'm not that kind of guy. It's not like I have his phone number to just call him. I don't even have a cellphone. I just had to find a place for my sister and I that was safe.

The hotel attendant escorted us to a room in the back of the building on the second floor. The outside of the hotel was sketchy, and the lobby was decent, nothing super impressive, so I assumed the rooms would be okay at the most. Surprisingly, the room was amazing. Actually, let's keep it real, it was high key bougee. Like I walked into a different world. As soon as we walked in, we felt as if we were in a totally different place. Alexis and I couldn't believe it. The carpet was clean, the bedding looked white and freshly ironed, the towels were softer than I expected, and the room smelled good. There was a unique fold on the toilet paper I had never seen before. There was a huge flat screen television on the wall and complementary water on the nightstand. To be honest, it didn't matter what the room looked like unless there were rats and roaches running around, we would have taken anything.

I told Alexis to take a shower while I go back down to tell the guy thank you again for the room.

I rush downstairs, as I don't want to leave Alexis alone for too long.

"Hey bro. Thank you," I said as I went in for the "dap-hug."

"No problem, man."

"I appreciate it. I didn't get your name."

"It's John."

"Thanks, John."

"You're welcome. It's for one night only and I'm not going to be here tomorrow morning. There will be another lady with red hair and she's not as nice as me. She'll call the cops on you, and I might get fired if she finds out I let you stay here. So, when you leave, take the side exit. Not the front door."

"No problem. Do you know where we can get something to eat?"

"Yea, there is a pizza place down the street."

"Thanks."

I ran back upstairs to the room.

Alexis and I sat on the bed in silence for a few moments. It had been a long day and I could see the stress on her face. I didn't know what to say to make her not worry because I was a little worried myself. It's bad enough that I got myself in this situation but dragging her into this didn't seem right.

"What are we going to do tomorrow, Brian? Where will we sleep?" Alexis asked quietly.

"I'm not sure, but that's tomorrow's problem. Let's relax, get some food, and just enjoy the nice room. We'll get some pizza and hopefully it doesn't cost a lot of money. We can pretend it's a mini vacation, remember when we used to take those back in the day? You were kind of little."

She nodded. "I remember a little bit." It had been such a long time since she went anywhere that wasn't school, the park, or the store with our mom. Hopefully, this felt like a little adventure because we were staying in a hotel. By the time she was old enough to really enjoy our vacations, our dad was back in jail and our mom was working all the time. I hated this would be the childhood she remembered.

We left for a little while to get the pizza and came back to the hotel room for the rest of the night. We flipped through the T.V. channels looking for something to watch until we got tired. The T.V. had Netflix, something we haven't had in years. We could watch some of the new shows that were out and some of the old shows from a few years ago. I don't know what tomorrow will bring, but I am going to relax for the rest of the evening. I thought about calling my mom, but she would probably try to trace the call and come get us. I couldn't let that happen because I had to reach my father and the only way I knew how to do that was through my uncle. I know she's probably worrying, but hopefully she doesn't call the police. However, from watching different things on T.V., I also knew that I only had a few days before they considered us missing. They probably wouldn't think I was missing since I'm legal, but Alexis is a different story. Hopefully mama trusts that I'm not going to let anything happen to her. I'll call her as soon as we reach Uncle E.

Yo, it's morning already? This was my first thought when I opened my eyes to the sun glaring through the window. I don't feel like I got a good night's rest at all. I didn't stay up late but I feel like I just went to sleep. Alexis is still asleep, so I'll quietly lie here so she can get as much rest as possible. We'll leave once she wakes up. I wondered what we would eat for breakfast. We have some money left, but we need to save that. Who knows how long it will take for us to get to our uncle? We should just eat some of the snacks we brought. That'll be better. Just as I was getting up to get something from my bag, Alexis woke up.

"Good morning, Lex, how did you sleep? I didn't wake you, did I?"

"Hey no, I've been up for a few minutes. I tried to sleep a little longer, but I couldn't force myself to go back to sleep and the sun is too bright, even with the curtains closed. So, I just laid here with my eyes closed."

"Okay cool. Wait? It just hit me. I remember when I was in the fourth or fifth grade, our family took a trip to Disney World."

"And what does that have to do with anything?"

Here she goes with her smart comments. "Listen, at the hotel we were staying at in Florida, I remember there being breakfast near the lobby. There should be something like that here. It's worth a try," Alexis said.

"Let's sneak down downstairs to see what we can find."

"Didn't you say the guy yesterday told you we had to leave through the side door? And not to be caught by the lady?"

"You must not be hungry," I said, since she was giving push back.

She rolled her eyes, "I mean…. let's make it quick," Lex said.

We made our way to the lobby. I could see the lady with red hair standing near the front entrance. That's the lady John told me to stay away from.

From the bottom of the stairwell, I whispered to Alexis, "No risk, no reward."

She smiled and said, "Let's do it."

"Let's go back to the room, really quick."

We ran back to our little bougee room. "We have to create a decoy."

"What do you mean?" she said.

"We have to take the lady's attention away from the lobby and place it on something else. I saw something like this on an episode of *Power* when I was at Donovan's house."

"Okay Tariq, I mean Brian." We both smiled at each other. "Why don't we just go down there, grab the food and run," she said.

"No, I don't want to mess the relationship up with John. You never know when we might need him again."

"True, that's a good point."

"I need you to run to the entrance of the hotel. Go to the lady and say there is a huge black snake in a parking spot."

"You really think she will believe that?" Lex asked.

"Can you think of anything better?"

"Ummm, not right now."

"Lex, I'm sure she will walk outside to see if you're telling the truth. You distract her from the lobby area where the food is, and I'll throw food in our bags. Then I'll head back to the room. You meet me there after but make sure you put something in the side door, like a brick or twig, so you can get back in the room."

"Wow, Brian, that sounds like a good plan," Lex said.

"Cool, let's eat really quick then head out of here."

Shockingly, the plan worked. At first the lady told Lex to leave, or she was calling the police. But Alexis told her the snake was about to get on a blue Nissan. Not knowing that it was the lady's car. She ran out there with a baseball bat that was behind the front desk. We met back in the room, ate, and left before the lady with the red hair ever saw us.

About five minutes later, we started walking. But I had no

idea where to go. I knew there wasn't a bus coming until tomorrow. I thought that if Lex and I just started walking back to the bus terminal, maybe they would allow us to sleep there. On the way, I saw an older man crossing the street in front of us, pushing a shopping cart full of empty soda cans. His clothes were rough. He had the dirtiest blue jean overalls I've ever seen. It was like something out of a movie. His hair was thinning, a few bald spots at the top of his head, reddish skin, and his boots were wet and soggy looking as if he had been walking through swamps all day. He was walking very slowly, as if his back was hurting. Usually, I wouldn't' ever speak to a stranger, especially not with Lex around me. What if he had a knife on him and tried to cut me for food? I was desperate, and maybe he knew where we could get food or of a local shelter in case the bus terminal told us we couldn't sleep there. It was a chance worth risking. I want to keep walking, but something in my gut is telling me to speak to him. You never know. He may know more about the city or how things are here.

"Hey, Sir, how are you doing?" His eyes lit up when I spoke to him.

He stopped walking and said in a thick southern accent, "How ya'll doing?"

"Nothing much, I saw you walking and wanted to speak to you. I'm Brian and this is my sister, Alexis."

"Alright, I'm Rufus," he said with a huge grin on his face. More than a few teeth were missing, but I could tell he was good people by his energy. "Thanks for saying hello. I'm on the way to the store. Ya'll be careful out here, ya hear me?" the man said as he began walking again.

"Yes Sir, we don't mean any problems."

"I know you don't. Just want you both to be careful. You don't sound like you're from these parts. Where you from boy?"

"Me and my sister are from D.C."

"D.C.? Like, Washington, D.C.?" he said.

"Yes Sir."

"What the hell are you two doing out here? Excuse my language young lady. Where are your parents?"

"It's a long story. Are you from here?" I said.

"I'm from Memphis, Tennessee. Came here many years ago to work at a plant. Things got a little rough. Heavy drugs, alcohol, then my wife left me. It got dark and I fell off for a while. But now I'm getting myself together. Been clean for fifteen months now."

"That's pretty good. Sorry about what happened."

"It's alright, things happen. Okay, now get to it son, what are you all doing down here in Carolina?"

"Just traveling through," I said.

"Sounds good, young man. You all enjoy your day. Be safe," he said while pushing his cart toward a gas station."

Something in my gut is telling me to ask him a question about a bus. "Sir, wait. Do you know when the bus is going to Atlanta?"

He looked at me directly in my eyes. The man's soul was piercing, and it made me uncomfortable, however I couldn't look away. I could see that he had lived a lot of life.

"I used to, but the times change all the time. Son, it doesn't look like you have a watch. Why is that?" he asked.

I looked down at my wrist. "No Sir, I don't have one at the moment."

"How are you ever going to know the time if you don't have a watch? Here take mine."

"No Sir, I can't do that."

"Young man, please take it."

"Sir, I can't do it," I said, resisting, knowing if I had a watch at the bus terminal, I probably would've planned a little better and we would've never missed the bus.

"Little girl, please tell your brother to stop playing and take the watch."

Alexis looked, gave me a nod, and said, "Take it, Brian."

I reached my hand out for the watch. The man placed his watch and a pen in the palm of my right hand.

"Sir, what is the pen for?"

The man said, "Every person should have a watch and pen on them at all times. A pen to right down his goals and a watch to keep him on track."

I couldn't get the words out of my mouth fast enough.

Alexis said, "Thank you, Sir."

"No problem, the last lesson I have for you is that a man and woman must always look to add value to other people. That's something that is lacking more now than ever. People deserve much better mentorship and role models."

"How can we add value to you?" I said, hoping he didn't ask for money.

He responded with a huge grin from ear to ear. "Do you have any food that I can have?"

Alexis reached in the bag and grabbed our last blueberry muffin from the hotel and handed it to me.

I truly do not want to give him our last bit of food. We worked hard for these muffins. Almost went to jail for these muffins. Maybe I'll split it in half and give it to him. Naw, he is probably hungrier than us. This man gave me a watch, a pen and dropped gems of wisdom. I mean, I could give him all the stuff back though. No, no, I'll do what's right.

I really don't know what to say. I'll just say something my coach told me at the award ceremony after football season ended. "Sir, thank you for everything. Please take this muffin as a token of our appreciation."

"Keep an open mind young fella, you'll go far." Then the man smiled, nodded, and walked away. I hate to give up that blueberry muffin. But for what he gave me, I don't know if I could ever truly repay him.

CHAPTER FIVE

W e spent the better portion of the morning walking around, looking at the neighborhood. There wasn't really much to do where we were, and I wanted us to stay within a five-block radius of the bus stop. I didn't know what time the bus to Atlanta left tomorrow, but I planned to be there bright and early in the morning. I don't know what we'll do about a place to sleep tonight. Maybe we can go back to the bus station and sleep there until morning. In the meantime, we can rest at this park. It seems safe.

Alexis loves swings. Every time I see her play, I feel a little jealous how innocent she is and how none of what has happened has impacted her like it has done me. Maybe I'll get on the sw…"

"…What's up big dawg?" I heard someone say, out of nowhere.

I jumped up. "Aye, you can't be sneaking up on people like that. I almost punched you in the face, man!" I looked this guy up and down. He looked about the same age as me. Maybe a few years older, and a little taller. His clothes were dirty, and the bottom of his shorts had holes in them. At first, I was about to grab our bags, get Lex and ignore him, but then I remembered I had a shirt with holes and sometimes I wore dirty clothes too.

"Nothing is going on; I'm just sitting here. What's up? Is there an issue?" I asked, defensively.

"Nah, nah, I'm just asking. Are you and that girl together? I saw you two walk over here."

"Why do you want to know? You don't know us, and if you mean brother and sister, then yea. She is my little sister, and I'm willing to die protecting her."

"Bro, relax. I'm not going to try anything. I'm just wondering what y'all doing out here in the middle of the day. She looks a little too old to be on the swing. You running away from home or something?"

I hesitated on giving an answer. That was a weird question to ask, and I wondered who sent him. I just looked at him, confused and wondered why he was asking me so many questions.

"I'm sorry. I know it's weird. I'm a stranger and I just came over here asking a bunch of questions," he said, as if he could read my mind. "I'm Tommy. I'm at this park all the time and I've never seen you here. No one really comes to this park anyway unless it's somebody running away or waiting on the bus or something. I don't mean any harm, man."

"Oh, okay." I let my guard down a little. He seemed cool. "Okay…good to meet you, Tommy, I'm Brian and that's Alexis. We're not from here, we're just taking a break until we leave tomorrow."

"Where are you from?"

"D.C. We're going to Atlanta, tomorrow." I wondered if I had told him too much.

Tommy looked at me confused, "D.C.? What are you doing here if you're going to Atlanta?"

"Well, we took the Greyhound up here and missed our bus when it stopped for a break. We're hoping we can get on the one going there tomorrow."

"Oh, good luck with that. There are normally a lot of people trying to go to Atlanta this time of the year. I've been a few times. It's not crazy far from here."

"Oh okay." I shook my head. Missing our bus already added more time to our trip than I planned. I was beginning to feel disappointed.

"You know, I know someone going to Atlanta tomorrow. I wasn't going to go with him, but I can go and I'm sure he'll let you and your sister ride along."

"Really!? No way, man, you for real?"

"I'm dead serious, bro," he said, then he paused as if he had something else to say but he was nervous. "But first I need to tell you I'm pretty much homeless. I just know the right people. There isn't a homeless shelter nearby, so I sleep here most nights, over by that huge, brown tree. My friend doesn't live too far from here, just in the next neighborhood. His mom doesn't like me, so I can't stay with them. One day she came home from church and caught me smoking weed in the bathroom, bro she lost it! She threw my clothes at me and told me to leave. I thought it was a bit much, but it's whatever. Now, whenever I need a ride, I just show up when she leaves for work," Tommy said.

"Damn, I hate that happened to you. I see what you're saying about the ride, but it sounds risky. What if he doesn't have room?"

"He always has room," Tommy reassured me. "He's a loner. I mean, you'd have to be to befriend a homeless person like me."

"This sounds good and all, but I feel like you're playing." This sounded way too good to be true.

"Nah, I'm not. I know you don't know me, but you can trust me. I'm just out here trying to make it. People help me all the time and I have a chance to finally help someone else."

"Okay, let me tell my sister really quick."

There was a woman sitting in the grass reading her book close to Alexis. I told her all about what Tommy said and tried my best to convince her that it was a good idea. I felt like this was a sign that everything was going to be okay. She was not convinced, but because I wouldn't let it go, she went over to talk to Tommy.

After talking to him, she pulled me to the side where Tommy could no longer hear us and told me she thought Tommy was shady. She said she didn't like the way he was always looking at the ground during the conversation, pretending to kick twigs and dirt or when he did look up, it was to check behind him, like something was coming. I got defensive, but she stood her ground. I didn't see what the big deal was.

"Lex, Tommy is cool. There were ants around his shoe, that's what he was kicking at. There is no reason why we shouldn't trust him, he's good people Lex. You're tripping."

"No you trippin!" Brian, this is crazy. It's not like this guy said he was taking us somewhere to sleep and we would meet his friend there. He said we had to sleep in the park and in the morning, he would take us. I don't trust that dude, if shady was a person it would be him," she said.

"You can trust me. I know it's been a crazy few days, but we haven't gotten hurt. Before you know it, it'll be morning and we'll be headed to see Uncle Eric."

"I don't like it!" She folded her arms.

"I know you don't, but it'll work out. This is my call."

"Whatever, Brian," she said as she rolled her eyes at me.

"Yo, Tommy, we're good. Let's do it."

Tommy seemed extra excited when I told him we were going with him and his friend tomorrow. That made Alexis even more suspicious.

Later that evening, the three of us were sitting together underneath a tree in the corner by the parking lot. I had bought everyone pizza, but this time I didn't get any extra toppings since I had to get a bigger sized pizza for all three of us. I looked down at my watch. It was 8:37 p.m. but it felt much later. We had been moving all day and the heat of the sun made us even more tired. Tommy shared a little bit of his story with us. He'd been homeless for about a year. His mother overdosed on the drug heroin and died when he was younger, and his father was in jail for double murder. I felt sorry for him. I'm sure Alexis did too. It made me grateful that both our parents were alive. Sure, there were people that could take care of us temporarily, but how long before we became a burden and ended up on the streets as well? I can't help but think about what Donovan had said to me about people having it worse off than me and that I should be lucky to have a mom who cares. I brought myself back to reality. Though it was true, it was too late now, I'm already on the road to find my dad and there was no turning back.

"We should get some rest because we have to get up pretty early tomorrow," Tommy suggested.

He was right. I leaned up against the tree and Alexis laid her head on my arm. It had been a long day. Within minutes, Alexis was asleep. I was going to try to stay awake, but my eyelids were getting too heavy and I don't know how much longer I can fight it.

"Brian! Brian!! Wake up!" Alexis taps me on my thigh. "Our bags are gone and so is Tommy!!"

CHAPTER SIX

W*hat is happening!?* I can't believe this. I looked around where we were sitting and started moving the leaves and tree branches that were around us. Our bags had to be here somewhere. No way they were gone. This couldn't be real. Don't tell me that this man stole our bags and took off. I can't believe this. I have to be the biggest fool to have let this happen. "C'mon man," I said under my breath.

"They're gone, Brian. Everything is gone! All the money's gone! Tommy was shady and probably took them as soon as we went to sleep. I told you I didn't trust him. You only listen to me when it benefits you. You got us in this mess," Alexis said while trying to hold back her tears.

"I know Alexis. That's on me. That's my fault." All I could do was shake my head. "I don't know why I didn't listen to you."

"Because you don't listen. You think you have everything figured out and you have to control everything. We're in this place now because you said you had it all figured out." She sat on the ground with her arms folded and started screaming. She was trying not to cry. I felt like she was about to cuss me out. I feel like crap for trusting that fool.

"I know. I know… the money was in the bag too. I knew I

should have put it in my pocket. I don't know what to do," I said as I paced around in circles, trying to think of a plan.

Alexis said nothing, she just moved the dirt around with a small stick, trying to calm down. Maybe I should just take her to the police station, and we find a way home. This was clearly a bad idea. "I think we should find the nearest police station and have them call mama."

"What?!" She looked up at me with a confused expression on her face. I thought she would be relieved.

"Yea, it's time to go home. We don't have any money; we don't even have a place to sleep. We missed our bus because I messed up. I own it. We should have never come. Everything I thought was a good sign, turned out not to be, and now we've been robbed. We're lucky to still have our lives."

"Yea, it was a bad move, but I don't know about going home just yet."

Alexis was just about to say something else, but then she looked past me like she saw a ghost.

"Brian, no way. Look!"

When I turned around, it was Tommy. He was standing on the opposite side of the park. He still had on the same t-shirt from the last time I saw him. It seemed like he was searching on the ground, probably looking for something that fell as he was running away. He had to be an idiot; he should be long gone from this park knowing he had our stuff.

"This damn fool! I'm about to go get our stuff! Stay behind the trees so no one sees you."

"Are you sure? What if he has a weapon?" Lex asked.

"I am a weapon."

"Okay, tough guy, where was that energy yesterday when you were acting like Tommy was the new bestie?"

"We'll talk later. I gotta go."

"Brian," she said.

"What's up?"

"Don't walk up on him. Go from the side. If he sees you, he'll start running and we will probably never see him again or get our stuff back," she said.

"I got you," I said and nodded in agreement.

I felt drained. I don't know why I keep messing up. I wish I could just switch into a character, like from a movie, or show, and be someone else. Because I was failing badly at being Brian and taking care of my little sister. I must show Alexis that I can do this.

I walked toward his direction, but more so from the far left, just as Lex said. Very quietly, even getting low and crawling at times. I can't risk him spotting me, I'm sure he didn't think we would be up this early. Tommy had his back turned, so he didn't see me coming. I should have waited until I got up closer but when I was about 20 feet from him. I said, "Aye man!!"

He turned around surprised to see me, dropped the paper bag that was in his hand and took off running.

"Aye man, stop! Stop where you're at!" I yelled. "Why did you steal our stuff! It's over when I catch you!"

I took off after him! He was much faster than I thought he would be, it's like he had been in this situation before. But what he didn't know was that I ran track and played football in high school, so I have speed too. I'm so determined to catch him. At first, he ran through the parking lot, and I followed close behind. Whenever he turned, I turned. Whenever he slid across a car, I slid too. I almost ran clean over an old lady walking her dog and ended up tripping over the leash. Almost falling face first, but I caught myself and kept going! All I needed was for him to be in arm's reach and I could grab him.

"Give up man, it's over," Tommy said.

"Yea right!" I was getting out of breath but there was no way that I was going to stop chasing him. We ran out of the park, and I followed him down the street. I can't focus on my running to catch up to him because it just hit me that I left Alexis in the park, alone. He seemed to be picking up speed, and I was slowing down. I was getting too far away from the park, and I needed to stop, but I couldn't let him get away.

"Thank God," I gasped out. He eventually got tired began walking, and I almost caught up to him, but then, out of nowhere, red and blue lights started flashing nearby. *Whoop Whoop!* "Stop right there, stop right where you are!" I heard them say.

Damn! It's the police! I looked in front of me and Tommy was turning a corner, full speed.

"I said stop! Stop! Don't make me shoot!"

What the—why are they even after me and now they are talking about shooting. There is no way I'm stopping. If I do, it could all go wrong. Why are they targeting me? Hell no! I can't stop. I looked back and they were still in their car yelling. I've lost sight of Tommy. I found my second wind, which pushed me to run faster. After gaining more distance, I slipped through this old, rusted door of what looks like an abandoned building. I need to find somewhere to hide and catch my breath. *Damn. Alexis!* I need to get back to my sister. It's too early in the morning for this.

I looked around, and the building I was in was two stories, so I went upstairs. I found a room facing the side I came in on. It had a window, so I looked out to see if I could still see the cops. They were still there, standing by their car. I don't understand, why they were yelling for me to stop and not Tommy. Hopefully they'll leave soon, and I could get back to Alexis. *Lord, please don't let anything happen to her.* This day is getting worse and worse. I should have never left Washington, D.C. At this rate, I'm going to end up in jail or dead because I couldn't sit still. This is really my dad's fault. If he would have just come back home, hell if he would have called, I wouldn't feel like I need to go find him.

What are they doing? Leave man, damn. There's big brown rats running around in here and there is a black spider about the size of my hand spinning a web three feet from my face. I gotta get out of here. I'm ready to risk it all at this point.

I watched the cops for what seemed like an eternity. They are seriously just sitting there. I don't think I can take much longer than this, I'm about to give up and walk outside. It's already been about forty-five minutes. Wait. I see movement. No way. They are backing up. Must've got a call about something more important than chastising a teenager. Or maybe they thought that if I had the guts to go in this building, I must be crazy! Thankfully, they pulled out and went a completely different direction of the park.

Okay cool. It should be safe for me to leave now. I don't know where Tommy went or how far I was from the park. I was running so fast to catch Tommy that I wasn't paying attention to how far we were going.

By the time I made it back to the park, the sun was at its highest, and I was sweating bullets. It was still summer, but the sun didn't have to be this disrespectful. The wind blew a little, and I instantly smelled a musty stench that had to be coming from me. I smell like I haven't taken a bath in days. I looked around for Alexis and didn't see her anywhere. My chest got tight. I would never forgive myself if something happened to her.

"Alexis!!" I started screaming. "Alexis! Where are you?" I noticed some bathrooms on the other side of the park and decided to check in there just in case she was hiding. Opened the first stall, no sign of Lex.

"Alexis!" To my relief, she came out of the last stall, crying tears.

"Alexis! Are you okay?!" I pulled her in for a big hug and looked at her up and down to make sure she wasn't hurt. Her eyes were red and puffy.

"I'm okay now. I thought something happened to you because you never came back. I didn't know what to do so I just hid in here."

"I know, I know. I was chasing Tommy and then the cops came out of nowhere and started yelling for us to stop. I had to hide in some nasty, abandoned building."

"Why? Before you left, you said we should go to the police station to get help. That could've been the chance."

"Yea, but there is a difference between us voluntarily walking into the police department to get help and them stopping me because they think I did something wrong. At that point, they don't want to hear anything I have to say. So, the chances of you being out here by yourself longer were high."

"I don't understand, if you need help, they should help you."

"I know, but it's not always that easy, Lex."

"Okay, so do we go to the station now?"

She caught me off guard with that question. I wanted to because I was tired of being in this mess that I got us in, and I didn't know what else to do. "Umm, I guess so. So, we can go back home."

"Well..." she started but hesitated and looked down at her feet.

"Well, what?"

"I don't think we should give up. I think we should keep going?"

I looked her up and down a second time to make sure she was in her right mind. I was confused. Earlier, she was fussing at me for trusting Tommy and now she wanted to keep going.

"Alexis, I don't have a plan or know what to do next. You see where I've gotten us so far. All our money is gone, all of our stuff. We don't even have anything to eat. We need help."

"We do, I agree. But you wanted to find daddy for a reason and if we give up now and go home, we may never find him. What if we never see him again?"

"I feel you, but do you have a plan that I don't know about? We're still hella miles away from Uncle Eric. We can always go back to the bus station to see if we can get a ticket, but I don't know. It might be too late."

"Maybe. Yesterday when we were walking over here, I saw this sign that said we feed the homeless. Turn here! It's not too far from the hotel. Technically we are homeless, and we do need to eat. We can go there, and maybe get some help so we can keep going. I just don't think we should give up. We are closer to uncle Eric here than we are at home."

I thought about what Alexis was saying. It seemed risky, and I didn't want to put her in danger, however she really wanted to continue and if we stopped, we both would be disappointed. I didn't want to let her down anymore.

"Okay, listen. We will continue, real talk, but if something else crazy happens… we are going to the police station to tell them what's going on and pray they take us home."

"Okay! Deal!"

She was oddly excited. It worried me because things weren't so great, but it was comforting to know that she still believed in me.

CHAPTER SEVEN

The place that Alexis was referring to that fed the homeless ended up being a storefront with a restaurant in the back corner. Normally people would get their food and leave but I noticed it had two small tables with chairs toward the front just in case someone wanted to stay for a while. As we walked in, we introduced ourselves to the storeowners; an older couple. They looked like they might be in their sixties. Even though they were older, their energy was surprisingly high, they came off like they were on two red bulls and three cups of coffee, but I could tell it was natural after a while. Probably because they were in great shape. The old woman looked as if she could bench press more than me. Probably retired athletes or something, I'm not sure, but I've never seen a couple this fit. I approached them cautiously and told them that we had been robbed at the park. We were without money or extra clothes. I explained to the couple that we were trying to get to our uncle in Atlanta and I didn't want any trouble, I just wanted to see if I could get some food for my sister and I.

She gave us some food and told us to have a seat, then she said she was going to see what she could do about getting us some clean clothes. As she walked away. I noticed a bright red sign with black writing hanging up on the wall by Alvin Toffler that read:

"The illiterate of the 21st century will not be those who cannot read and write, but those who cannot learn, unlearn, and relearn." This quote stuck with me. Even though I love my father very much, he still possessed some very bad habits. The biggest one was his constant drinking of alcohol. He would always sit in his brown chair, right in front of the TV, and get drunk throughout my childhood. He would always say, "Come here Brian. Go get me a beer out the fridge." I would be his personal servant for hours on hours. Running toward him whenever he called my name. "Yes, Daddy," I would say. Never receiving a thank you. Like it was my duty as a son to tend to his every need, and looking back on it, it was lame as hell. Even though I know there are some things he taught me, there is still so much I need to learn as a man. I refuse to treat my children and wife the way he treated our family.

"Young man, are you okay?" The older lady interrupted my thoughts.

"Yes ma'am. I was just reading the stuff on the wall." I pointed to the sign.

"Oh, that. My husband says that all the time. He grew up a little differently than I did. I don't know what I would do without my handsome hubby, Walter. Is the food good, how about you little lady?"

"Yes ma'am," we said in unison.

"Tell me about this uncle of yours, where does he live again? Atlanta?"

"Yes ma'am," I answered.

"Does he know you're coming? I'm sure he's worried."

"I don't think he knows we're coming. We don't know where he lives," Alexis blurted out.

I shot her a firm glance. These people are feeding us and everything, but we do not know them. This could become another Tommy situation very quickly.

"I think it's time for us to go. Thank you for the food, ma'am," I said as I tried to finish the last bit of my grape soda.

"Hold on, hold on," The lady patted my shoulders to sit me back down. "I'm not going to hurt you. I told you I would help you and that's what I want to do. Calm down. You're safe here."

I just stared at her. Trust didn't come easy with me. But I didn't try to get up. She pulled a chair up and sat down at the table with us.

"Now tell me about this uncle, maybe I can call someone to locate him and he can come get you. I take it you don't know how you were going to get to him."

I nodded. "I thought we could take the Greyhound but so much has happened and I'm sure by now we have missed the bus."

"I see."

"His name is Eric Johnson, he was in the military, and he sent us a postcard about a year ago telling us he was living in Atlanta with his wife, Melissa. He's our father's brother."

"Where is your dad?"

"I don't know exactly. I believe he's in Houston, Texas. We were hoping if we got to our uncle then he would be able to tell us where he is. We haven't spoken to either one of them in a long time,"

"I see," she said again. "You said his name is Eric Johnson and he lives in Atlanta?"

"Yes, ma'am,"

"What does your uncle look like?"

"Umm... he's tall. Maybe as tall as me or an inch or two taller, you can tell he works out. You know what? Actually, the guy in this picture. Luckily, I didn't leave the picture in the bag. I had kept it in my right back pocket. It had gotten kind of soggy from all the running I had been doing. "The picture is a few years old but I'm sure he looks the same."

She smiled, "Well, if we're going to help you get to your uncle, we want to make sure it's the right person and not just someone pretending to be your uncle. Suga, I'll be right back. Let me go make a phone call."

As soon as she stepped away, I mean-mugged Alexis and said, "Why'd you tell her that about Uncle Eric? Now she knows we were just wandering the streets. What if she calls the police or something?"

"Me?" She looked surprised. "You just gave her all this information about Uncle Eric. And besides, I don't think she is going to call the police. I think she really wants to help us."

Just as she said that, a cop walked in. I got nervous. I knew this lady was going to call the police. I nodded at her and then headed back to where we were. I sat up in the chair, trying not to look suspicious. I couldn't help but to look at the cop. She was gorgeous! She had a mean-sexy look about her. I almost winked at her the first time we made eye contact. "Misses Officer, Misses Officer," I whispered under my breath, remembering a Lil Wayne song I used to play. I stopped and tried to act normal before she put me and my sister in the back of the police car outside. Dang, she was looking right at me now.

"How y'all kids doing today?" she asked. Then she went to the window and grabbed the wrapped plate that the cook had just placed down.

I don't want to come off suspicious or anything, "I can't complain, Ma'am and you?"

"Good, don't complain. Nobody wants to hear it. I'm great. Just getting some of this good food before my shift starts. You two have a good day."

"It just got better."

I watched her walk back toward the front. She stopped to say something to the lady and then looked back at us. I thought the lady was telling her what was going on with us but she walked out the store. Maybe the cop was going to get back up in case we tried to run. I would try and run if they tried to take us in. Even though I'm sick of running today.

"See, she didn't call the cops on us."

"You don't know that. She could be coming back."

Alexis rolled her eyes. The store owner walked back over to

her. I hope she has some good news for us that doesn't involve her police friend.

"I have some news for you two."

"Yes ma'am."

"Your uncle doesn't live in Atlanta anymore."

My heart dropped. I tried to keep my breath steady and listen to the rest of what she had to say. If he wasn't in Atlanta, where was he?"

"Did he die or something?"

"Oh, God, no! He moved. He lives in Charlotte, North Carolina. A lot of military guys retire at the base down the street and move out to Charlotte. It's about three hours from here. When you started describing your uncle to me, he sounded really familiar. His wife has a pie company.

"A pie company?"

"Yep. They sell pies throughout the entire state of North Carolina. He drives trucks for their company with both of their faces on the side of the truck. Wait. You guys might be in luck. Your uncle should be coming by today."

"Hey, baby, they don't deliver today. Remember? They only sell out the main bakery in Charlotte on Fridays," a loud voice from the front yells out.

"Oh, yeah! You're right, Walter. Shoot!" The lady looked up, staring in a distance. "I've got a plan. Walter, can I talk to you in the back?"

"Sure, honey."

Alexis and I stared at each other trying to figure out what's going on. "Do you think they are going to call the cops?" Alexis said.

"Honestly, I have no idea. They seem like good people, but you never know. I appreciate the food, though."

"Me too."

"Maybe we should start looking for ways to get out of here in case they call the police," I whispered to Lex.

"Yea, or we could just bounce out of here now."

"True, that's not a bad idea, Lex. Let's get some water and roll out. Hopefully we can get out of here before they come back."

Just as we started walking to the front door, I heard, "Where are ya'll going?" It was Walter's voice.

Lex and I turned around very slowly. "Ya'll just going to leave without saying anything?"

"Sir, I thought you both were going back there to call the cops. We've come too far to give up now," I said.

He laughed, "Cops? Heavens no. I was young and full of fire once. I get it. Running away from home is not a good choice, but we figure that you both had to have weighed the options and leaving must've been the best one."

"You're right, Sir, this is the best option we could come up with."

"I don't condone running away, but we want to help you find your uncle. I'll stay and hold down the store..."

"And it's only right that a queen takes you to Queen City. Grab your stuff, we are going on a little road trip to Charlotte!" The lady said.

"Ma'am, really. You don't have to."

"No, no, no. I insist."

"Ma'am, we can't do it. I don't even know your name."

"My apologies sweetheart, my name is Miss Mary. Family is and always will be important young man. You two go to the bathroom and wash up. We've got a three-hour drive ahead of us and if my calculations are correct, we should arrive right before the bakery closes for the weekend."

Alexis looked at me and said, "This can't be real."

I couldn't believe it either. I smiled and whispered, "See, I told you to trust me."

She rolled her eyes and we both went toward the bathrooms to prepare for the next part of the journey.

CHAPTER EIGHT

I opened up the door to her 1999 Black Honda Civic. I noticed there were three kettlebells in the back seat.

"Oh honey, you can just put those in the trunk." She popped it open from the button on the side of her seat. "I got you."

I pick up the thirty-pound kettlebells one by one. I've always been fake strong. You know when you see people that are big but can't lift a finger? Yea, that's me. I had no idea how this lady was able to carry this much weight and at her age.

"Y'all two get in. We have to hurry if we want to make it to the bakery in time."

Alexis and I jumped in as fast we could. "Ma'am, can you crack the window for us?" It was hot as hell. I almost burned my finger on the medal buckle of the seat belt. Must be 100 degrees out here. It's taking forever for the A/C to kick in. Only ten minutes into the drive and I'm sweating bullets.

"Ma'am, I have a question. How old are you?"

Alexis side knees me in my right thigh.

"What?" she said. The kettlebells and her biceps are throwing me off. "I'm trying to see something," At first, I thought she was old, but maybe she just has wrinkles.

"Well baby, I can't tell you my age. It's improper for a man to ask for a woman's age, ya know?" she said in her sweet, southern voice.

"Oh, my bad, Miss Mary."

"Just know I'm older than you think. And leave it at that," she said while laughing. "In life, you always want to stay a few steps ahead, and an easy way to do it is by putting in the extra effort upfront. Believe me honey, I love to watch T.V. and sleep in like everyone else in the world, but I know if I waste time doing those things I won't become a better me. And I love what the gym is doing to my body, but it's also doing wonders to my mind. Walter and I are thinking much clearer about things since we started running and working out for one hour every day. We're constantly improving. That's what it's all about kids, and that goes for anything in life. You want to compete against someone? Compete against yourself. Become a better you every day. And that's why I'm stronger than your brother now," she said to Alexis.

"Yo, hold up, I thought we weren't competing." Brian and Alexis begin laughing.

"Miss Mary, thank you for taking us to see our uncle. Even if we never find him, I want to thank you for everything."

"No problem, baby. Y'all get some rest. We have a while before we get there."

She didn't have to tell me twice, my eyes closed before she got the last word out. I was tired from running around and all the drama today.

Suddenly, I feel Alexis tap me on the chest. "Brian, wake up!"

I feel like I just went to sleep. "Huh, what's going on?"

"Miss Mary said we will be there in five minutes. I couldn't sleep. I'm so excited."

From the back seat, I hop up and take a look in the rearview mirror. I lick my fingertips and slick back my eyebrows. I'm excited too. The moment is feeling a little surreal. It's been so long since we last saw our uncle. I wonder what he will think of us. But

I can't help but wonder why he didn't ever check on us? Will he even remember us? Maybe this is a bad idea. I'm second guessing this whole thing now.

We drive up and park in a parking spot directly in front of the bakery.

"Whew, we got with twenty minutes to spare. Yes! Give me some!" Miss Mary said.

I hesitated to give her a high-five at first, because I didn't want her to break it, but I knew it was the least I could do for driving us all the way to Charlotte. "Thank you, Miss Mary."

"You're welcome, love. Let's get you two in there safely, then I have to get back to the store. Walter left his glasses in this car and can't drive home without them.

I take a deep breath, grab Alexis' hand, and we stepped out the car and begin walking to the front of the bakery.

As soon we walked in, we're greeted with the fresh smell of cookies, pies, and every kind of cake you can think of. It literally smells like Heaven here. I see a lady with her back turned to us. Alexis looked at me and said, "I think that's Aunt Melissa."

"I can't tell if that'd her or not."

"Yep, that's Melissa, sweetie. I've known her for about a year now," Miss Mary said. "Hey girl, good to see you!" Miss Mary yelled out to Aunt Melissa.

"It's good to be seen! Mary, girl is that you? What in the world are you doing here?" Aunt Melissa asked.

"I think you may know these two," Miss Mary said.

As we get closer to the counter, the side door swings open, its Uncle Eric. He wore jeans and a collared shirt, but the way they fit looked like they were made specifically for him. I looked down at my overly baggy white T-shirt and felt suddenly lame and for the first time, I felt dirty... too dirty to talk to him. He looked very serious and as he walked toward the back of the bakery, kind of like he was looking for something or someone, I was frozen, I couldn't take another step forward. Now he's walking toward us.

"Brian? Alexis?" When he spotted us, he looked really confused.

"No way? Am I tripping?" Uncle Eric cheerfully said. "What are you all doing here? Is your mom here too?"

He put the pies he was carrying on the counter and opened his arms to give me a hug. He glanced down at my clothes and frowned. "What's going on here?" Come here, both of you."

We ran and hugged him. He kneeled and asked again, "What's going on, where are your parents?" I could tell he was concerned by looking at how dirty we were.

"It's just us," I spoke up.

"Hmm?"

"We left home so that we could come and find you. I know it sounds crazy, but I was hoping you knew where our dad was."

"What do you mean you left home? You ran away?" he asked calmly.

"Yea, sort of, we were going to take the Greyhound to Atlanta where we thought you lived but then we missed the bus when we got off to use the bathroom. We were stuck in Fayetteville for a few days before meeting Miss Mary and her husband Walter." I glanced at Miss Mary; her tears were rolling down her cheeks. "Miss Mary are you okay?"

"I'm okay, sweetie. I have to get back to the store," Miss Mary said.

Eric stood up and walked over to Miss Mary and gave her a hug. "Miss Mary, thank you so much for bringing the kids here to the bakery. I owe you and Walt some pies next week. Hold me to it."

"I sure will Eric, ya'll take care," Miss Mary said as she headed to exit out the front door.

"Thank you, Miss Mary!" Alexis and I yelled out.

"Anytime suga!"

"Eric, we have to get back to work, don't you see all these customers waiting," Aunt Melissa said.

"Give me one second, Sweetheart. Don't you see my niece and nephew standing right here?"

"Yea but hurry up. Ya'll can have your little family reunion later," Melissa harshly said.

"Good to see you two," Uncle Eric said with a huge smile on his face. "Well, it's a good thing you got stuck in North Carolina, because we moved from Atlanta a little over a year ago. Does your mom know you're here?"

"No, she would have never agreed to let us come. I left her a note and we left while she was at work. She works a lot since... you know, dad went away."

"I know," his eyes softened. "You two can come with me and we'll call your mom and get all this sorted out."

We began walking to the side door that I had seen Uncle Eric enter through earlier. "Hey baby, I'll be right back. See you at home."

"Whatever Eric," Aunt Melissa said.

"Don't mind her. Let's get you to taken care of."

Uncle Eric probably drove the biggest truck I'd ever seen in my life; people didn't drive big trucks where we lived. Shoot, most people walked in D.C. or used the metro. His truck was huge, not monster truck huge, but big! I even had to step up on a chrome side rail to get into it. It was white with tinted windows and black leather seats.

"Seriously, y'all doing okay?"

I glanced at Alexis. Her big brown eyes begin to tear up. "Yea, we're fine," I said. "We just need our dad. We need our family back together. It's been so hard for us."

"Wow, I had no idea. I'm sorry for not seeing you all or calling. I feel like crap. After I retired, I got really focused on the bakery and Melissa. That's no excuse, I dropped the ball. I'm so sorry."

It was completely silent for the next twenty minutes.

. . .

We pulled up to a gate guard, Uncle Eric gave him *the nod* and he let us through. His neighborhood was full of mansions and exotic cars.

"This is our home," Uncle Eric said.

This is crazy! We pulled onto a perfectly laid brick driveway with a three-car garage. Nice pretty green grass, damn near perfect, no patches anywhere in sight. Don't even get me started on the house. I kept glancing over at Lex, "Close your mouth." I said as I tapped her. Even when we did have money, we never lived in a place like this. Before we got out of the car, I asked him about our dad. "Do you know where our dad is?"

He paused for a moment before he responded, "I do not. I know the area he's supposed to be in, but I don't know exactly where he is in that area. He's in Houston, Texas. But I don't have his address or anything. It's been like a year since we last spoke."

"Okay." I didn't know what else to say. He didn't know where our dad was either, so we came here for nothing.

"I'll help you find him, don't worry."

"You will?"

"Yes, of course. But we do need to let your mother know you are safe and after I get you settled and cleaned up a bit, we'll look for him. I know people everywhere, so hopefully he's not that hard to find. Besides, I don't want you running away from here in the middle of night to look for him. No more of that. It's not as safe out there as you think."

"I know, we've had people help us, but we also got robbed and I got chased by the police. We could use your help Uncle E."

"I got ya'll now. You alright, Alexis?"

"Yes, sir. I'm fine. Just tired."

"I bet. Your Aunt Melissa just got here. Let me see if she brought home food for us, so y'all can eat and get some rest."

Aunt Melissa seemed anything but glad when she walked through the door, she didn't even smile. She just stared at us. Eventually she said a dry, "Hey," and rolled her eyes before she walked back into the kitchen. I have no idea why she disliked us so much. I noticed that Uncle Eric saw her attitude as well but shrugged it off.

"Hey baby, were you able to pick up some food?"

"I'm warming up some oatmeal on the stove."

"Give me one sec, guys. Let me talk to your aunt."

He was gone for about ten minutes. I hoped he asked her why we had to eat oatmeal for dinner. We were used to eating worse, but I feel like this was some type of punishment. We're family, I'm not sure why she would do us like that. I get the feeling she doesn't want us here.

"Okay, come with me," Uncle Eric said, and we followed him up the stairs. "The house has six bedrooms, I'll show you around later. We don't have any kids yet, so we have two guestrooms. I'll put both of you in your own room for the time being."

Four of the two bedrooms were upstairs. I wondered if the master bedroom was downstairs. He opened a door closest to the stairs on the left and told me it was where I would stay.

"Brian, there is a bathroom attached to this room." He pointed to a door in the corner. He continued, "There are clean towels and plenty of soap in there. I'll bring you clothes and I have a new pack of boxers that should fit you. I'll put the stuff on the bed, so it'll be there when you get out."

"Okay, thank you."

"Cool, let me know if you need anything in the meantime."

Him and Alexis turned to leave the room and I heard him tell Alexis that Aunt Melissa went to go and get her some clothes so she could get cleaned up too.

This room seemed like it was the half the size of our home in D.C. It was big enough to fit a double bed and a chair in the corner, with a tall dresser and two nightstands. Don't get me started on the bathroom. Two people could stand between the toilet and the tub and still have room to move around. Everything was spotless, and shiny white. I moved the shower curtain to turn the water on and almost got wet because the shower part was on. The showerhead was huge. I couldn't wait to get in there. The soap was already in the tub and the towels were on the counter. I stood there for a minute. This was like a real vacation, the bathroom and bedroom reminded me of the hotels we used to stay in.

Knock, knock!

"Come in," I answered.

"Is everything okay, Brian?" It was Uncle Eric.

"Yea, I'm just sitting here. Is Alexis, okay?"

"Yes, Melissa is helping her get her stuff together."

"I need to call my mom." I remembered that I was supposed to call her when I got to the house.

"I already called her. She went to work. Boy, is she upset with you, but she is relieved that you're okay."

"Do you think she's going to come and get us?"

"No, I told her not to. That I would take care of you. I know it's important for you to reach your dad. So, she's okay? She's going to call back when she goes on break or when she gets off."

"Do you know why my dad didn't come back for us when he got out of jail?"

"I'm not sure," he paused for a little while. "He might be embarrassed. I'm not making excuses for him, but he's been in jail for a few years. He probably feels like he let his family down by not being able to be there for you all. He's missed a lot of your lives. Nothing is worse than a man's pride. Whatever you do Brian, never let your pride get the best of you and cause you to lose everything… family, a friendship, or an opportunity."

"I get it, but didn't he know we needed him. We don't care about him going to jail. We just wanted him to come back home to us. We barely have anything now and my mom works so much that I never get to see her. He just left us."

I stopped talking when I heard my voice start to crack, I didn't want to start crying but I started to feel really sad, all of a sudden.

"I know, and hopefully when we get to your dad, he can give you some answers. I know it hurts. We both grew up without our dad and I always wondered why he didn't want to be a part of our lives."

"I've never heard daddy talk about him, I just assumed he died."

"Well, he did die, a long time ago, but after we had already become adults. But we don't know much about him because he was never there for us."

"Wow. I had no idea."

"You hungry? Your aunt made a big thing of spaghetti for all of us, then you can relax the rest of the night."

"Okay, cool. I have a question. What does that quote on the wall mean?" I pointed above the T.V.

"Oh, that one." He got up to look at it and smiled hard as hell, "It's one of my favorites. It read: "When you stay ready, you don't have to get ready."

I learned this firsthand when I was a young Second Lieutenant in the military from my Brigade Commander, Colonel Smith. He would mention this to me constantly during my first ninety days in the unit. He could see that I didn't grow up in the most educated environment and just barely made it through college to commission as an officer. He told me that I was missing an essential element to becoming a great human being. The ability to prepare before execution. I usually just showed up and did halfway decent things, but he told me that if I just took a little bit more time to prepare on the front end, I would be unstoppable when it was my time to shine, and I would be more confident in my abilities because I had already rehearsed so much. The interesting thing is that his audio also matched his video. Have you ever seen someone that tells you one thing but does the complete opposite?"

"Yea, most definitely," I laughed.

"Well, I have too, but that wasn't the case with Colonel Smith. While other leaders would shy away from exercising with their soldiers, he never did that. He would always lead from the front, in whatever it was, six mile runs in the Middle East or rehearsing for big speeches in front of large crowds. Brian if you want to be the best and win in everything you do, you have to remain disciplined and put the extra work in. Even when you're tired or hungry. Remember that proper preparation separates winners from losers. Never think that life is filled easy wins, cause it's not. Doesn't work like that. If you don't take the time to prepare you will lose every time. And I can see you're a winner, both you and Alexis are. You gotta sacrifice ideal time for maximum success. This concept applies to everything under the sun. School, your future career, even girls."

"Girls? Unk, you playin right?"

"No, I'm serious, you see a girl you like.... Take the time to notice what draws her attention. Maybe she likes to read, or exercise, or write poetry. Whatever it is, figure it out, and use it as a conversation starter. Instead of just walking up saying, "Hey my name is Brian and I play football."

We both busted out laughing.

"I feel you Uncle E, but how do you know if she is the one or not?"

"You don't. But if you do the work on the front end, before you say anything to her, it will make things a lot smoother when you approach her. People don't know this but the most important decision you make in your life is the one you choose to spend your life with. That person will either inspire you to grow into greatness or they will push you towards constant failure."

"I appreciate it, Uncle Eric. Is it cool if I use your phone to call my friend back home?"

"Yea, but don't take too long. I don't want your food getting cold."

"Yea, most def. I'll be down in a sec."

I ran to the bathroom and shut the door.

Ring, ring… "Hello!"

"Yoooo, Donovan. What up bro?"

"Brian, is that you? No way. What up boy! You lucky, I never pick up unknown calls. Your mom came by here looking for you a few days ago. You know I ain't say nothing. Y'all good though?"

"Mannn, it's been wild.. Let me tell you about it."

After speaking with Donovan for ten minutes, I couldn't put the phone down. I know I told Uncle Eric I would be down shortly, so my food is warm but that's why God invented microwaves. I'll be straight.

"Yea, so that's what's happened so far."

"Yo, that's crazy man, y'all really out here wildin'. But I'm glad you made it to your uncle's crib."

"Yea man, me too bro, how you been?"

"Everything is going okay. My grandmother has been pretty sick lately, so I'm dealing with that. As you know, my Big Mama has always been there for me and my family. Other than that, I've been going to sit down with Principal Thompson every other day."

"No way man, I thought you didn't really rock with him like that, especially since he suspended you for that fight earlier in the year."

"I didn't bro. But after you told me how he helped you, I decided to put my pride to the side and go see him in his office. He's even trying to help me apply for colleges."

"Donovan, that's dope as hell. I told you he wasn't a bad guy man."

"Facts, real cool dude. He came from worse conditions than both of us and made it out, bro. He took risks, failed, and saw it as an opportunity to learn. Told me that every setback is a set up for a comeback and I believe in that man.

"Yea, Principal Thompson is always droppin gems bro."

"No doubt, he helped me realize that I could easily make something of myself I just have to let go of the "poor" mindset and that P.O.O.R. stands for *Passing Over Opportunity Repeatedly*."

"That's tough bro. I never knew any of that, but it makes sense to me. That's why I'm out here."

"Exactly bro. I respect you for taking the leap. Going to college will be mine. No one in my family has ever made it that far. I'll be the first."

"I'm proud of you bro. Keep seeing Principal Thompson. I'm sure he will continue to give you good advice."

"Will do, bro."

"I'll hit you back soon bro. I gotta eat and check on Alexis."

"Okay cool. Bro, be safe man."

"I got you."

CHAPTER NINE

I can't believe it's been a little over a week since we first got to Uncle Eric's house. He said he was working on locating my dad, so we didn't go to Texas looking lost. I guess it was a good idea. It's not bad here. Plenty of food and the air conditioning never goes out like how it did at our home. It's funny though, Uncle Eric and Aunt Melissa are total opposites, but it works for them. Uncle Eric is more of a talker, okay he is loud as hell. You can always hear him yelling from across the house and Aunt Melissa doesn't say much, at least not around Alexis and me.

My stomach started growling out of nowhere. So, I rolled out of bed, brushed my teeth, and walked downstairs to the kitchen.

"Hey Brian, yea I was hungry. Where is Uncle Eric and Aunt Melissa?"

"They are at the bakery."

"But it's Saturday."

"Yea, I know, Uncle E told me someone rented out the bakery today for a baby shower, so they had to be in early to set it up and cook."

"Oh, okay, how was the movie last night?"

"Movie... movie... Oh man, let me tell you about it."

"So, I always thought Uncle Eric was perfect. Well, until last night at the movie theater when he was about to fight the manager because he told them NOT to put butter in his popcorn."

"No way, you're kidding right," Alexis said while laughing.

"I wish I was. It all started when he returned to his seat with a huge bucket of popcorn. We were having a debate on who was better, Lebron or Jordan - he swore Jordan would destroy Lebron if they played in the NBA at the same time. I don't see it, but whatever. When the previews began rolling. We both shut up because we wanted to see what new movies were coming out, and that's when he stuck his hand in the bucket and put that first bit of popcorn in his mouth. He spit it out on the row in front of him. All I could hear was, 'Oh, hell naw!' Then he told me to grab my stuff and come with him. We walked up to the counter, and he said, 'Who's in charge?'

The guy says, 'Sir, I'm the manager on duty. How can I help you?'

Uncle Eric then said, 'Why in the complete hell did you put butter in my popcorn when I clearly told ya'll not to.'

'Sir, our apologies, we can fix it.'

"No way, please tell me you are playing with me?" Alexis said.

"Check this out Lex, then Uncle Eric yelled out, 'It's too late now!' He dropped the popcorn and acted as if he's going around the counter to grab the guy. Dude glasses were all fogged up and everything, almost pissed on himself. I grabbed Uncle E before he could get to the guy, then security ran up and throws us out of the movie theater, telling us to never come back.

When we got in the car, we had a long talk. I was so surprised he had really went off like that. He admitted that he had a temper, and he had been going to some therapist.

"Wowwww! At least he is taking time to work on his attitude. Still can't believe he started trippin' like that."

"Me either. I told him that Donovan had a pretty bad temper as well but it improved a lot since his older sister introduced him to meditation."

"Wait, Donovan, meditates?"

"Yea, he does, and it think it actually works. I thought it was crap until I saw him exploding one time after we lost a football game on an interception followed by a touchdown from the other team. He was pissed! We all were. But he came into the locker room throwing stuff around, yelling at our other teammates before the coaches walked in. Afterwards he went to the car and meditated for ten minutes. When I saw him, I seriously thought he had gone to smoke."

"But Donovan doesn't smoke, right?"

"Exactly, I was so confused," I said, as Alexis started laughing.

"So, I asked him how he got so chill. At first, he didn't want to tell me but eventually he told me he meditated."

"Wow, that's cool. I had no idea it would work like that."

"Yea, it takes time. The first time I did it. I thought it was a waste of time. But I stayed with it. And now it helps me control my emotions. The better you control your emotions, the less people can control you. And the best thing is that it's free. Doesn't cost a dime."

"Yea, that makes sense."

"I shared that story with Uncle Eric, and he said he wanted me to show him how to do it when he got back from the bakery. I can't believe he was opened to listening to me give him advice. I hadn't really seen that before. Usually it's a one way conversation with older people. He mentioned that, 'You can never stop learning. No matter how old the other person is.' He also mentioned to me that he could tell we were hurting from my dad being gone for so long and recommended we go see his therapist next week. "How do you feel about that?"

"I don't see it as a bad idea. If it's working for him, it may be helpful for us too. I know we talk about how much we miss daddy, but maybe talking to someone about it could help,"

"Okay, I'll tell Uncle Eric. Let's watch that new scary movie downstairs."

"Yesss, let's do it."

. . .

A couple of days pass. "Miss Ashley, I'm answering all your questions. What more do you want from me?" I let out a sigh. "I'm getting really tired of this therapy mess."

"Brian, I've been doing this for years. I know when someone is telling me their true feelings and when they aren't. I really want to help you."

"No. I'm good," I grunted. "I came up here to get help finding my dad, not sit with you and I've been here too damn long. School is going to be starting soon for Alexis and then we'll have to go back to D.C. I really don't have time to be talking to you. I need to get my family back together. Uncle Eric isn't helping, instead he has me here talking to you."

"Okay, we're getting somewhere. How do you know he's not helping you? Did he say that?" Miss Ashley asked me.

"No, he didn't. But he said he was getting in touch with his friends that live in Houston to get help with locating my dad and I haven't seen any progress."

"And why do you think he's not helping?"

"Because..." I sucked my teeth. "It's been weeks. They haven't found him yet?"

"I'm not sure, but it looks like you want it to happen in your time and because it doesn't you think they aren't helping. That may not be entirely true."

I guess she was right, but that's not what I was trying to hear. I've been waiting every day for my uncle to come and tell me that he found my dad and he was taking us to him. I don't feel like it has to be in my time, but maybe I do."

"For homework, I want you to talk to your uncle and tell him how you feel. It's okay to ask him to keep you in the loop. It's also okay to feel disappointed with the news. But I want you to exercise patience. Can you do that?"

"Yea." I was still annoyed.

"When you see your father, what are you going to say to him?" she asked again.

"I'm going to ask him why he never came back to us." I

decided to answer her with more than I don't know, maybe she'll stop asking.

"And what if you don't like what he has to say, I want you to think about that,"

"Why? Why would he say something that I don't like? I'm his son." I felt my face get hot.

"Brian, I recognize that what I just said to you may upset you, but I want you to think about a few things. You're an adult now, so I can be real with you. No one, but your father knows why he didn't come back to you when he got out of jail. I'm sure there are assumptions from your friends and family. But only he knows. There can be a number of reasons and there is a possibility that he says something that makes you have sympathy for him, and it's possible he might say something that makes you upset. More than you are now. You need to prepare in case it's not such a happy reunion."

"What should I do then?"

"Don't allow your father to dictate how you feel in that moment when you first see him. It's going to be a series of feelings in your body at that time. Remain calm. Breathe. And find joy and keep it on the inside of you and regardless of what happens, don't let anyone steal it from you?" Miss Ashley told me.

"How do I find joy? I don't even know where to begin."

"You can manifest it, think about it and do things that bring it towards you until they become your reality. Pain doesn't always last, but you have to be willing to let it go. You've been through a lot. Remember that tough times don't last always, but tough people do. You and your sister have shown incredible perseverance. I look forward to sitting with you again, okay?"

"Okay. Thank you. I'll see you next time, Miss Ashley."

My uncle had taught me to always say thank you to people, not just to think it. Whether we paid people to do stuff or not, they didn't have to do anything for us. Miss Ashley was definitely being paid but I know I gave her a run for her money some days. Some days I wanted to talk, and other days I wasn't in the mood. I did have a lot of pain that I needed to let go of, but I don't know if I had enough time for what Miss Ashley wanted me to do.

When I got outside, my uncle was waiting for me. He always stood outside of his car until I came outside. He was old school like that, it didn't matter where we were.

He never waited in the car. He got in when he saw me coming.

"Unk, why were you standing outside the car in the rain on the hottest day in June?"

"Never mind that Brian, be who you are no matter the circumstances. How was it today?"

"It was alright. How long do you think I have to keep seeing her?"

"It all depends on what she says and how long you'll be here? Are you ready to stop?" Uncle Eric said.

"I don't know. I'm just waiting to go to my dad."

"I know, I'm waiting for a buddy to call me back. He's calling tonight, so hopefully I have some news for you and Alexis."

"Okay, that's good." I felt myself getting excited. Finally, we were getting somewhere.

"You're looking real sharp in that shirt man. It's a nice color on you," he said.

"I appreciate it Uncle E."

The second day we were with Uncle Eric, he took Alexis and I shopping. I threw those clothes we came in away because there was no saving them. Even though no one said it, they smelled horrible. I know Alexis was excited to get new stuff too. He bought us about two weeks' worth of clothes and shoes. I looked down at the light blue, Ralph Lauren polo I was wearing. It was fitted and since Uncle E and I began working out in the home gym and running in the neighborhood, it fitted tight on my arms and chest.

"Thanks. I really appreciate you for getting us these clothes. You didn't have to do anything for us. You really could have sent us back to my mom," I responded.

"Yea, I could have but I wanted to help. I was in the military for most of your life and due to the demanding schedule, I never got the chance to spend a lot of time with you two and now you're a young adult. I wish I had got to you and Alexis sooner. But God always works everything out for a reason."

"Yea," I didn't say much, but I did wonder what life would look like for us once we made it to our dad. "I had good intentions when I left with Alexis. It just didn't work out that way."

"I know you did. But remember intentions aren't everything. You my friend have to do a better job of planning and weighing the second and third order effects of your decisions before you make a move. You two have been blessed, but you could have easily been harmed on your journey. Also, what if your mom had to miss work to come find you but her job wouldn't allow her to come back, because she had to miss too many days. She would be in jeopardy of losing her home by not being able to afford the bills. Or if she would've called the police and reported you for kidnapping."

"Yea, I didn't think about all that."

"Right, most people don't. I'm not perfect, I've made mistakes in my life as well. But I try hard not to ever make the same mistake twice. The world is tough. It will eat you up if you let it, you have to remain strong and vigilant through the ups and downs. Your mom is the strongest woman I've ever met in my life. Because even through the storms, and trust me Brian, rather you knew it or not, there were many storms between your mother and father, she would always prevail. He would continue to make the same dumb mistakes and go to jail when you were growing up but she never left you hanging did she?"

Looking down at the ground, I said, "No, she didn't."

"C'mon man, look up at me. I'm not getting on to you. But you owe her a lot more respect than what you've been showing her. She never stopped supporting you, and taking care of you, while working many jobs. I get it. I too know how it feels to look up at the stands in a game and not see either one of your parents. But Brian, you must notice that the only reason she wasn't there is because she was working to keep lights on and food in your stomach. Awareness is key. The good thing is you're not in this alone, document your lessons learned. You never know who could benefit from it.

"Together we are stronger," Uncle Eric said as we walked in the house.

"What do you mean, together we are stronger?" Alexis asked.

"Good question, Lex. I need you both to always share your successes and lessons with other people as well. All people, regardless of race, gender, or religion. We need more unity in this world, and you could be the one to bring it. The life lessons that you only gain from experience and mentorship. Role models are needed and I'm hoping I can be that for you."

He waited for me to say something, but I didn't.

"Your aunt's sister and brother-in-law are coming by this afternoon for a late lunch. We might all go to the fair a little later if it doesn't rain."

I sighed heavily, "I hope she's not like Aunt Melissa."

He asked, "What does that mean?" like he didn't know his wife was mean. I saw Alexis walk away quickly towards her room.

"Brian let's talk downstairs for a minute. You're going to pretend like you don't see how she acts with us; she doesn't want us here."

"That's not true." I could tell he was trying to convince himself.

"The water got cold the other day when I was showering, I swear she did something to the water heater. It has never gotten cold."

"Go on. I'm listening," Uncle Brian said.

"She makes pies every week for Mrs. Mary's restaurant and never makes any extra for us. It's little stuff and the way she looks at us, like we are taking up space. It's true. You're just choosing to ignore it."

"Brian, I acknowledge your feelings and thoughts. Also, I can see how those things may frustrate you. But what you're saying comes off disrespectful and rude. Your Aunt has nothing to do with the water running cold. Sometimes I forget we have family here and truth be told, I take long, hot showers. Uncle Eric laughed. "Like I'm at some five star resort in the Caribbean, straight up forgetting I have bills to pay. Melissa gets on to me all the time."

"Yea, but what about the pies and the way she looks at us. Uncle Eric, you can't tell me you don't see it."

"To be honest with you Brian, I don't. If you want some pie man, you better speak up! Yea, Melissa isn't the warmest or the most welcoming person, but she still makes sure you're fed every day. You always have clean clothes and clean bedding, and it's because she's doing laundry when you're not looking. No one in this house minds helping you, but you have to think the best of people until they do something blatantly wrong to hurt you. If you don't, you'll miss out on establishing really good relationships."

"Yea," I tried to say that as calmly as I could. I didn't really have a lot of people talking to me about how I behaved or what I said, so it was a little uncomfortable. But I appreciated him listening to me.

As I was walking upstairs, I heard Alexis and Aunt Melissa having a conversation in the room. I took a few steps and noticed that the door was almost shut but had a small crack where I could make out the voices. I'm usually not nosey but I couldn't help but put my ear on the door. It wasn't often that I heard Aunt Melissa speaking and needed to make sure she wasn't yelling or getting onto Alexis for something I did.

"...that will help you a lot. I had to learn the hard way," Aunt Melissa said to Alexis.

I had no idea what they were talking about. I just know I had to pee so bad, but the bathroom was across next door and if I walked by, they may here my footsteps and I still gotta make sure everything is good with Lex.

"Yea, that makes sense. But Aunt Melissa how did you do it?"

"I had to speak up. There is so much power in our voices. I grew up like you, shy and afraid to voice my opinion to people, especially when it was a family member that needed help. I didn't want to get told off. That's how it was back in the day."

"I love my brother, but sometimes he makes bad choices. Not terrible, but the ones that could've been avoided."

Dang, they are talking about me, I'll chill out here but I'm busting in if she tells her why we missed the bus in Fayetteville. That's supposed to be our secret.

"Alexis, trust me, your uncle can be the same way. I've had to tell him a few times to relax. He's been like that since we got married. I love him, but he can be a little extra at times. I don't think I've ever told anyone this story but when I was close to your age, I don't know, around thirteen years old or so. No, no I was fourteen. I remember because it was around my birthday in September. There was a time when I wish I had spoken up sooner about the issues my big sister was having. When she was around sixteen, she had met a guy named, Frank. He was about five years older than her. My sister was crazy about him and so was our family. He was funny and good looking, but I always knew something was off with him. I used to hear him curse my sister out over the phone, she always had it on speaker, not knowing I could hear it from my room across the hall. After about five months of dating, Frank introduced my sister to drugs. Hard drugs. My dad had no idea. I always knew. She started to act different. From the beginning, I could tell that wasn't acting like herself. My room didn't have a T.V, so I would go in hers when she wasn't home. There I would find needles and pills behind the headboard and under her bed, but I would clean it up before my dad could ever see it. He would've been furious, and my sister would've been in trouble, probably on punishment for months. Daddy didn't play that mess. He believed in working hard and staying out of trouble. He worked constantly; we hardly ever saw him. Then one Sunday, my dad came up to the kitchen to get a morning coffee and there my sister was, mouth open, laid out on the floor. The night prior she had overdosed on fentanyl. I remember when the ambulance came. Her face was pale white, lips were dusty and cracked, she didn't even look like herself. This happened around my birthday, one year after our family met Frank. I'm still hurting from this. I could've helped my sister if I would've just told my dad. That's all I had to do." Her voice begin to crack a little.

Wow, I didn't know Aunt Melissa had gone through something so tragic. I feel so sorry for her. I can only imagine how she feels to have lost her sister. I would be devasted if anything happened to Lex.

Aunt Melissa continued, "My dad would've got my sister the help she needed to overcome the addiction. But instead, I was quiet when I should've been my loudest. Don't be afraid to call something out that's wrong. I know Brian isn't doing anything like that and I don't see that ever happening with him or you, but you never know. All I'm saying is never be afraid to speak up and help those closest to you, especially family and friends. I hope something I said helps you grow even more as a person, Lex. I see so much potential in you."

"I'm so sorry for what happened to your sister, Aunt Melissa, please don't blame yourself for that. It's not your fault."

"Thanks Alexis. It took me a while to realize that. I'm still dealing with it, but I'm getting stronger every day. Telling you that story helps me feel better. I wasn't so open when I was your age, I saw it as a weakness, but as I get older and wiser, I appreciate transparency and recognize it as a strength."

"Hey, Aunt Melissa, can I ask you for a favor?"

"Sure, what's up?"

"Can you take me to the store? I really need to get something, something very important. You know?"

"Okay, I know exactly what you mean. I can take you now."

"Awesome, one sec, just gotta grab my shoes... hey, Brian, what are you doing?"

I couldn't do anything but walk in.

"Brian, are you okay?" Aunt Melissa said.

I came and sat on the bed next to her. I looked her in the eyes with tears and we hugged, and we cried for a while. I told her I was sorry for her loss and I'm sorry for everything that happened to her family.

"It's okay Brian, don't worry about it."

"It's not your fault," I said. "Aunt Melissa, I'm here for you."

"Thank you, Brian."

CHAPTER TEN

U ncle Eric always insisted that we always sit together at the table for dinner. I didn't think I could ever get used to this; we didn't even do it before my dad left. Uncle Eric later told us that he didn't eat with his parents for dinner growing up either, his situation was very similar to ours.

"I have an announcement," my uncle said.

I thought he was just being funny as usual, but Alexis seemed excited, so I attempted to act thrilled as well.

"What is it Uncle Eric, what is it? Did you find my dad? Tell us," Alexis said with joy.

Uncle Eric looked around the room, trying to let the anticipation build up. Not fooling anyone but Alexis. "Tell us, tell us Uncle Eric."

Aunt Melissa taps Uncle E on the arm, "Stop playing Eric. Kids, we found your dad."

"Really?" I asked.

"Yes, really, my sorority sister from college lives in Los Angeles and is the finance director for one of the basketball teams out there. You might not believe this, but she told me she ran into your dad at the grocery store. They didn't get a chance to speak but my girl is certain that it was him. They all grew up in the same neighborhood; her, your uncle, and your dad. She moved to L.A. as soon as she got her degree. We talk every day," Aunt Melissa said.

"Whoa, ummm, L.A., wow." I leaned over to Alexis and whispered, "L.A. is in California, right?"

She smiled and said, "Yes silly."

"Looks like we are going to California!" Uncle Eric said.

I've lived on the east coast my entire life. This was my first time outside of Washington, D.C., now they are telling me we're flying to Cali. I'm starting to get nervous. I've never flown before.

"Melissa, are you coming with us?" I asked.

"I was going to stay back and run the bakery while you guys are out of town. But... I can come."

"Bet. I would really like you to come with us," I said.

"Me too," Alexis said.

"Okay, so it's a trip. I'll book tickets tonight and we will catch the first flight out in the morning."

I can't hold my excitement or stop smiling. I hope he is as excited to see us as we are to see him. Why wouldn't he be? We're his kids.

It was a non-stop flight, about five hours from Charlotte. We all slept some, some more than others. Aunt Melissa slept the entire way there. She had worked from sunup to sundown yesterday. I knew she was tired when she walked in after work. She crashed out on the couch for a few hours before we sat down for dinner. Since being here I must say, I truly respect her work ethic. She's a beast! One of the hardest workers I know, next to my mom. If they ever went into business together, they would be dangerous. My mom likes to bake as well, but we never really have the money to get ingredients, so she doesn't do it much. But two years ago, she made a cake for my birthday, it was so good, Donovan is still talking about it to this day!

I like Uncle Eric and Aunt Melissa's relationship; I know they aren't perfect, but they make a good team. Always preaching how important ownership is in our community. Whether it's a business, a home, or even land, because as Uncle Eric always says, "Boy you better get you some land, they aren't making any more of it."

Who knows, maybe I'll start my own business one day, and get some land, and yea, build homes on it for people from my neighborhood in D.C.

When we landed, Uncle Eric picked up a rental car so we wouldn't have to take the bus or a taxi to the hotel. As soon as we got settled in the room, we sat down at the table and discussed many options to find my dad. From putting up "missing person" posters around the city, to going to the local police department and officially filing a report. That was my idea, no one went with it. My excuse was that I was tired and couldn't think of anything else. Alexis was the only person that found that funny, but I wasn't joking.

Finally, we decided to crash and regain momentum in the morning.

"Are you excited to see your brother, Uncle Eric?"

"Yea, I am. I haven't seen him in years. Prior to him going to prison, we would speak a couple of times a week. This will be a good reunion for all of us. How do you two feel?"

"Brian hasn't stopped smiling since we got off the plane," Alexis said.

I laughed, "Yea, it's going to be good to finally see him."

"Hey guys, check this out. I invited my girl Sasha and her son, Troy, to come out to eat with us for breakfast. We can pick her brain and ask her questions about what he looked like when she saw him, etc. Troy just graduated from high school like you, Brian, and is heading off to Howard University in a month or so."

"Okay cool, so he'll be in D.C," I said. "That's what's up."

"Yep, that's right," Aunt Melissa said. "Alright let's head to the restaurant, it's about a fifteen-minute drive from here. They will meet us there."

We all got into the Nissan Maximum that Uncle Eric got us as a rental car. He has plenty of money, I couldn't help but wonder why he didn't get an upgrade.

"Uncle E, what's up with this car? You know I'm six feet four, right? My head is touching the roof."

He started smiling. "Brian, you know you can't tell me how to spend my money. I gave you fifty bucks a week ago, so you could buy something from Walmart. I just wanted to see what you were going to do with it."

"Eric, what did he do?" Aunt Melissa asked.

"Brian, would you like to tell her, or would you like me to?"

"Naw, I'm good," I said.

"He spent all of it on damn skinny jeans," he said as he burst out laughing.

"I thought because we had been working out, I could switch my swag up a little bit."

"Now Eric, don't be hard on Brian. You used to wear big white T-shirts down to your knees when we were in college," Aunt Melissa said.

"Unk, say it ain't so." I grinned.

"And? So what? We went to school in Atlanta, that's what we all did. Anyways, here's the restaurant. Is that Sasha?"

"Hey girl," Aunt Melissa yelled out the window.

"Melissa!"

Before we could get out the car, Sasha ran up to the car to hug Aunt Melissa with the window down.

"Hey Eric, hey ya'll!" she said waving at us. "I'm Sasha. This is my son, Troy."

It wasn't often that people could look at me dead in my eyes, we were about the same size. He was a little bigger than me. And he already had a full beard. Was Aunt Melissa sure he just graduated from high school. Dude looked a smooth thirty.

"What's up bro, my name is Brian, and this is my sister Lex."

"Cool man. Welcome to L.A.," Troy said.

"Thanks, they tell me you're moving to Washington, D.C. soon?"

"Yea, I'll be at H.U. in the fall. You live there?"

"Yea bro, born and raised. I got you if you ever need anything while you're there."

"Bet, what school you heading to?"

This was the first time anyone had ever asked me this. I didn't really give much thought to college.

"Ummm, I'm not sure yet. I just barely got through high school, by the skin of my teeth. Still trying to figure it out."

"No doubt, I feel you on that. I was unsure too. I look forward to linking up with you there."

"Boys, let's head into the restaurant. Our reservation is ready."

Aunt Melissa, Uncle Eric and Miss Sasha had a great time catching up and telling wild stories from college. Uncle Eric has come a long way from white tees and baggy jeans. Miss Sasha said that my dad had a salt and pepper beard when she saw him. Dad always had a mustache when he was home with us, not a full beard, that's a different look for him. She also said that he was skinny. Like sickly skinny. I hope he's okay.

After about two hours of us sitting at the table, Uncle Eric received a text message from his good friend from the military, William, who's a cop in Charlotte. "Baby, see what William just said. He's been working with the LAPD to find my brother." He hands the phone to my aunt, who screamed. "I think we have something, see the address below for your brother. After you find him, let me know, I'm going to send these boys a gift card to *Applebee's*.

I was more ready than him. I gave Troy my address and home phone number, I told me to call me as soon as he got to D.C. Everyone said their good-byes and we headed out.

We pulled up to the address. The neighborhood we were in looked like the same type of neighborhood that we lived in back in Washington, D.C, expect slightly worst. This couldn't be right, my dad had to be living better than this.

"Is this it?" I asked, hoping he would say no.

"Yep. He should be in this building. Apartment seven, so it's probably on the first floor. I'm going to park the car. You two stay inside and I'll go see if he's home. Okay?"

"Okay," I responded, "I'll make sure no one tries to steal the car or anything."

"Stop playing," he laughed as he got out of the car.

We waited for about three minutes and Uncle Eric came back outside by himself.

"Where is our dad?" I asked him, hoping he was just getting dressed or something.

"I don't know," he sat down and took a deep breath. "There is someone else living here and he said the previous tenant moved out last week. So, it looks like we just missed him."

"Missed him? What the hell does that mean? What do we do now?" I tried not to get upset. I know it wasn't my uncle's fault. Maybe it was, maybe we should have left last week.

"Stay calm. We are in this together. Let's go to the hotel and I'll make some calls."

On the drive to the hotel, we passed by this nice park. Uncle Eric asked if we wanted to stop and get something to eat. He saw a hotdog and ice cream stand.

"Alright, but let's make it quick," I responded. Ice cream did sound good. The hotdog stand was in the middle of the park. It was at least a five-minute walk from where we parked. When we got there, I didn't see anyone there. Then I realized there was a person with a red hat reaching into a cooler behind the stand.

This is weird. Maybe Principal Thompson was right. Everything is starting to feel like I've been here before. Kind of like it's *deja vu.*

"Excuse me, Sir, can we get some hotdogs?" Uncle Eric said.

The man stood up, turned around, and said, "Yea, one sec," placing his index finger in the air.

We waited for about three minutes. Alexis asked me what the holdup was. I shrugged my shoulders.

"Sir, how much longer will it be? We are on a tight schedule."

"Shouldn't be much longer. We ran out of hotdog buns. I'm waiting for my partner to get back."

"Okay."

I tell Uncle Eric that maybe we should start heading to the hotel.

"We will give them five more minutes," he said.

Out of nowhere a man ran up carrying three big bags of buns. I can't really see his face because of the mask he was wearing. He pulls it down to get a sip of water. No way! is that... "Dad!" I screamed.

My knees got weak.

"Big bro!" Uncle Eric said as he walked up to give him a hug.

It was our dad. Right here at the hotdog stand. I couldn't believe it. We found him. He was just as speechless as we were. At first, I didn't know what to do, I stood there in silence just looking at him and Uncle Eric, celebrating as if we hit a half-court shot at the buzzer. Ten seconds felt like ten minutes. While Uncle Eric and my dad were jumping up and down, I happened to glance at Alexis. She had huge tears running down her face, upset was an understatement, she was enraged. She took a few steps back from where she was originally standing.

"Alexis. Come here sweetheart," my dad said, standing there with his arms spread out.

She didn't move. I've never seen her like this before.

"Lexy, Lexy, it's okay. It's okay. What are you crying for?" my dad said.

"Lex, we did it. We did. We found daddy!" I said.

"Lexy, come here baby."

She wiped her eyes and tried to clean up her face. "Hell no!"

Everybody's mouth dropped, including my dad's.

"Why shouldn't I just leave like you left us?"

"Baby girl this isn't the time," my dad said.

"When is the time then? she heatedly said. "Who the hell do you think you are? Leaving us alone. You didn't even call when you got out?" Her fist was clinched and if he was close, it would be a problem.

I know Miss Ashley said I would have many emotions running through my body. I was fine until I saw the way my sister looked at that moment. If I had to name Alexis' emotion it would be mad as hell!!

"Lexy, please let's talk about this," dad said.

Alexis was not budging. "Why didn't you come back to us?"

"What? What do you mean?"

"Why didn't you come home? You got out of jail and then you just never came home. Don't you love us? Don't you love us?" she repeated.

"Of course, I do!" He reached walked toward me, reaching out a hug, but I kept my arms folded. "I love both of you and I think about you all the time. I honestly thought you two were better off without me."

"You're a coward!" she said.

Things are boiling at this point; I can literally see fumes coming from the top of her head.

"Lex, let's talk about this later," I said.

"Alexis, you're right. I am! I am a coward!" he yelled, looking away from us. "Please forgive me. I know I hurt both of you and your mama. I messed up. I messed up bad. But I'm a better person now. I'm sorry."

"Why should we believe you?" I said stepping away and toward my sister.

"I don't expect you to just believe me. Let me show you. I'm different now. It took me a minute, but I see why your mother stopped answering my calls, and I can understand why she divorced me. I was angry at her for years and I took it out on y'all. I shouldn't have done that. I was a terrible husband and father. I went to jail and let the whole family down. I don't blame you for hating me."

"We don't hate you," I said as I walked over and hugged Lex.

She seemed to be calming down now.

I let out a deep breath. "We never hated you. We just wanted to know what happened to our dad and why he never came back to be with us."

"We thought you hated us," Alexis said.

"Hate you? Baby girl, I could never hate you or your brother. You are my kids. I told myself that one day I would work up enough courage to go back to y'all. Even if it took me years to earn your forgiveness. I was going to try with everything in my heart. I just needed to get myself together and then I got sick."

"Dad, what are you talking about?" I said.

"Yea, I didn't want you all to see me like this. Four months ago, I was diagnosed with lung cancer. It's still in the early stages, the doctor said it may be curable. It's caused me to lose a lot of weight, as you can see."

"Dad, I had no idea," Alexis said.

"Yea, it's neither of your fault and don't feel pity for me. I've done terrible things in my life. And you both deserve better."

"Dad, we all make mistakes. No one is perfect. Alexis and I never stopped loving you. We think about you all the time."

This time he walked to me. He hugged me and gave me a kiss on the forehead. He used to give me these hugs when I was younger. He said, "I love both of you so much. I'm sorry for what I did to you two, and your mom. No one deserves the amount of pain and suffering I caused. I should've been a better father and husband. This took a lot of courage. You get that from your mother. I'm proud of you."

Alexis and I were still crying, the moment felt surreal.

"Can you all give me another chance?" he said.

I looked at Alexis for approval, I was so proud of her fearlessness. Usually, I was the one who would always stand up to people. But this time, it was her. She gave me a slight nod when we made eye contact. I looked back at my dad and said, "Of course."

"Thank you" he whispered.

"Eric, how did you all find me?" Dad said.

"I didn't. The address we had, they said you moved last week. We just happened to stop at the park and here you were. You own this?"

"Yea man, I got a great deal. I saved enough money so I live in a better neighborhood now. Me and my girlfriend, Stacey. Hopefully you all can meet her." He looked at us.

"Girlfriend?" Alexis said, "So you and mommy aren't getting back together?"

"I don't think so, baby girl."

"Oh," Alexis said sadly.

He looked nervously around, "Where is your mama by the way?"

"She didn't come. She is still in D.C. It's just us," I told him.

"Oh okay. Well, maybe I'll see her again in the future some time. It'll be nice." He walked back over to the hotdog stand. "Let me get you all some food. You're hungry, right?"

"Yes!" Alexis screamed.

We all laughed. Daddy gave us the hotdogs and Alexis and I sat at a nearby bench to eat them. He said we could have as many as we wanted and would get us ice cream when we were done. I got myself two hotdogs. They were good. I could have eaten a third one, but I didn't want to seem greedy. Uncle Eric stayed by the stand while we were eating. I don't know what the two of them were talking about, but they were doing a lot of laughing and smiling at one another. Then Uncle Eric patted my dad on the back and gave him a hug. They hugged each other for a nice little minute. When they pulled away, it looked like my dad was wiping his eyes.

"What do you think Uncle Eric is saying to daddy?" Alexis asked. "He looks like he's crying."

"Not sure. Uncle Eric is really good at saying stuff that makes people feel good. He's probably saying something real encouraging, you know how he is? We both started laughing.

"He told me that he knew Daddy had a good heart, even

though he had made mistakes that got him in trouble. He was still a good person."

"Do you think he's a good person?" she asked me.

"I think deep down he is a good person. Do you think I would've gone through all this if I didn't think so? Hell naw!"

She laughed.

"We would definitely still be in Washington, D.C. if that was the case."

"Come on Lex, let's go get our ice cream," I said.

Our dad bought us some ice cream and told us about how he got the hot dog stand and what he had been up to since he got out of prison. He seems to be doing very well for himself. Uncle Eric said he was proud. We left him to finish his day at the park, but we made plans to get together for dinner later.

When we got back into to the hotel, I called my mom. It was easier to talk to her now since her anger with me had lessened. I still thought she would try to jack me up through the phone.

"Hello?" She answered on the first ring.

"Hey, ma. We made it to L.A."

"L.A.? I thought ya'll said he lived in Houston. Have you seen your father?" Mom said.

"Right, we thought so too, but then we got news that he lived in L.A. It's a crazy story how we ran into him…" I told her all about us going to the wrong apartment and then running into him at the park. She just laughed and said nothing surprised her when it came to our father.

"Your uncle bought me a plane ticket to come up there with you all. I leave here in the next week."

"Here? Los Angeles?"

"No. Charlotte."

"Dang, I wish you could come see Dad."

"Brian, I hope you know, I'm not getting back with your father. Your dad really hurt me with all his foolishness. There were good times, he was my first true love, we have a lot of history, but when it was bad… it was terrible. I told him plenty of times to let the streets go and just be with us a family. Like you didn't even see half the crap I went through. I can't go back doing the same thing, over and over again. That's insanity."

"Yea, I get it now, Mom. I didn't understand, but now I totally get it. I'm sorry he put you through all that mess. You want to talk to Lex? She's sitting right here."

"Yea, let me talk to my baby."

I gave the phone to Lex and laid back on the bed.

It wasn't dark outside, but I felt like I could use a nap, we were up early so that's probably why I felt so tired. I don't know what the future held for us, but I did know that my dad was now in it. Now that we've found him and I know he wants us, I'm not letting him go.

"Brian! Come here please," Uncle Eric yelled from the other side of the hotel suite.

"What's up Uncle E?" He was standing by the door with his back turned and didn't answer me the first time. "Unk, what's up?"

"Hey Brian, let's take a walk outside."

I nodded my head, uneasily; I had no idea what was going on. I felt nervous as if he was going to tell me someone in my family had died."

"Brian, do you believe in divine intervention?"

"Uncle E, I'm not sure what that is, school has never been my strong suit. You gotta explain that one."

Uncle E started smiling. "When I was your age, I had no clue either. I probably didn't know until about ten years ago. Well basically, it's when a miracle happens to stop something good or bad from occurring."

"Oh, okay, a miracle?"

"Yea, I know this may sound strange, trust me I get it, but I've been thinking about this for a week now, I just haven't said anything to you. I find it interesting that out of nowhere, you found enough courage to leave your home in D.C. and go out on your own to find your dad and bring your little sister with you. What was it, Brian?"

"To be honest, I kept noticing a sign at home that said, walk by faith, not by sight. It had to be there for years, but all the sudden it started to shine out at me every time I walked by it. It was freaky."

"It's like God was trying to tell you something all along. I'm glad you listened," Uncle Eric said.

"Yea, and before I knew it, I was literally telling Alexis that we had to go, and I was packing our stuff to leave out. We didn't even have a plan at first." I looked down at the ground, and said, "Which may not have been a great idea. We should've had a solid plan."

"Who cares? You know now. The first step is always the hardest. God was placing you on an assignment and you didn't even know it."

"What do you mean? Finding my dad was the assignment?"

"No, at least I don't believe so. Maybe it was part of it, but I don't think finding your dad was the assignment. Great job and all, you found him, but I think its deeper than that."

"Well, I did learn about myself. A whole lot."

"Really? Like what?" Uncle Eric said.

"I don't know where to start. Every moment has been a learning experience. Come to think of it, it's what you don't learn behind a desk in class. The first thing that comes to mind, is that I'm smarter than everybody says."

"Of course, you are. There is nothing wrong with you. Why would you think you weren't smart?"

"My teachers, teammates, coaches, everyone said I was slow."

"You're far from slow. Never let someone's judgment, cause you to second guess who you are. I stopped listening to fools a long time ago, you should too."

"Yea, I started to believe them. But this journey has taught me that not only am I smart, but there is no way anyone could ever doubt my effort. Just like in sports, I may not be the strongest, or even the fastest. But I'll be damned if I ever let someone out work me on the field or the court. It all relates to life now. My goal is to beat "them" to the spot every time. Every single time. Rather it takes me getting up a little earlier or working harder behind the scenes when no one is looking, so that when it's my time, I'll be more than prepared, I'll be ready to win. Now, I just have to relate it to other things, like school. I can be a beast Unk, I just have to give 100 percent effort in everything I do."

"Wow, you've learned all that on this trip. You probably had it in you this whole time and just needed something to bring it out of you. Seems like this assignment was it."

"Yep, I know everything will fall into place now. I've learned so much about myself on the quest to find my dad."

Tears begin to roll down his face. He stood up and walked toward the window, he placed his hands on his waist and let out a big exhale. At first, I thought he didn't want me to see him crying, but then he looked back at me, straight in my eyes to show me he was serious.

"Brian, I know you had no idea what you were doing, but you went with your gut. Even when things seemed challenging. Everyone in this world has a purpose. God puts us on assignments to guide us, direct us, toward our true purpose in life. From what you're telling me, it seems that God gave you an assignment to guide you toward your purpose, bring forth to light how remarkable you are as a young man and how amazing your sister, Alexis is."

"Right, it's all making sense now. He gave me drive and brought many people into my life, where I learned a major lesson from each one of them, including you."

"Look at you, Brian. I'm so proud of you. One last thing before you go back upstairs."

"What's that, Unk?"

"All this ends with you, right now, at this moment," he said passionately. "Your father and I didn't grow up with our father, you went years without seeing yours. This all ends with you.

Can't you see that? Not only have you found purpose, but when it's your time to have children, I trust and believe that you will be the best father a son or daughter could ever have. This is bigger than both you and me. The assignment will continue."

Just when I thought I was done crying for the day, Uncle Eric knows how to bring it out of me. I walked up to him, and we hugged and cried for what seemed like hours. I felt it in my soul that he was absolutely correct. The lessons I learned on this journey have prepared me for whatever life brings and I made a promise to him that night that I would change the narrative for our family .... for generations to come. The assignment will continue.

The End

ABOUT THE AUTHOR

Anthony Williams Jr. is an advocate for mental health along with being an established author for younger readers. As a previously troubled teen, he now dedicates his time to helping the younger generation gain the mindset to overcome adversity, remain resilient, and be effective leaders. In addition, Williams learned the importance of mental health and building foundations of trust from his life experiences as a military officer, where he was granted, 'The Defense Meritorious Service Medal' and 'The Honorable Order of Saint Martin'.

"Truly the most inspirational thing I've done for the greater good was serve as a military commander, leading an aerial delivery company that was accountable for the training, readiness, morale, and equipment of 150 personnel and their families."

From a background in the U.S military to cofounding a mental health therapy practice. His years in the service provided great inspiration for his writing and is where he was able to do most of his travelling. During his expeditions, he witnessed pain all over the globe, solidifying his mantra of 'everyone struggles.'

"What I've learned is that the most common denominator amongst all people, despite the color of your skin or where you come from, we all can relate to some to form of struggle. Rather its mental, physical, emotional, or financial, - regardless, we all experience struggle at some point in our."

Anthony Williams Jr. resides in the Washington, D.C. Metro Area with his wife, a talented therapist, and loving children.

You can find him online at:

www.anthonywilliamsjr.com

A NOTE FROM ANTHONY

Thank you for purchasing my debut novel. If I may ask a small favor, I would be eternally grateful. Please leave me an honest review on Amazon. As an author, I take pride in my work and welcome all feedback.

Respectfully,

Anthony Williams, Jr.